1980s
Quiz Book

1,000 questions for the whole family

www.ovingo.com

The golden rules of happy quizzing

1. It goes without saying that a quiz should be fun, so don't take these questions too seriously.
2. If you're playing as a group or a team, be flexible, allow for a margin of error in your friends' answers and look to give points wherever possible. Where a question asks for a year, allow a decade either way. Where it asks for a measurement, decide how big a margin to offer depending on how large or small the increments are.
3. The more generous everyone is, the more fun you'll have.

Suggested method of play for groups

To avoid anyone having to sit out and watch while one other person asks questions and another single person gives answers, appoint one question asker per round and one person who will receive all of the points from the whole team. Everyone can suggest answers and it's up to the person who receives the points to decide which answer to take (or use one of their own). At the end of the round, the question asker and the person choosing the answers should change until everyone has had a turn in each role, or you decide to stop playing.

This book is produced and published by Ovingo Limited
www.ovingo.com
©2016 All Rights Reserved

Quiz 1

1. In Knight Rider, what did KITT, the car's name, stand for?
2. Complete the 1987 catchphrase: "Nobody puts Baby..."
3. Which European city hosted the 1984 Winter Olympics?
4. Production of which rival format to VHS cassettes came to an end in 1988?
5. How many Oscar nominations did 1989's Driving Miss Daisy receive: five, seven or nine?
6. Which version of Windows was released in December 1987: Windows 1, Windows 2 or Windows 3?
7. Name the pianist who died of pneumonia in Palm Springs on 4 February 1987.
8. The world population was estimated to have reached what number by July 1987? 4bn, 5bn, 6bn or 7bn?
9. In which two cities were the 1985 Live Aid concerts held?
10. Which 24-hour television news channel launched on 1 June 1980?

Quiz 2

1. What was the name of Emmett "Doc" Brown's dog in Back to the Future?
2. Digging for which international rail link began on 1 December 1987?
3. Where were the first CDs produced on 17 August 1982?
4. Money for Nothing was a 1988 greatest hits album from which British rock band?
5. Which American actor, who went on to star in the television series ER, made his film debut in 1987's Return to Horror High?
6. Which 1988-born English actor rose to fame playing Ron Weasley in the Harry Potter film series?

7. In which year did Whitney Houston release her debut album?

8. In the UK, British Leyland launched what it intended to become the replacement for the Mini on 5 October 1980. What was it called?

9. The Soviet Union started to restructure its economy to become more like a capitalist country in 1988. By what name was that process known?

10. Name the monastic novel published by Umberto Eco in 1980, which was later filmed with Sean Connery, Christian Slater and Michael Lonsdale in lead roles?

Quiz 3

1. Which British actor, star of Rebecca, The Boys from Brazil, Brideshead Revisited and Marathon Man, but more often recognised for his theatrical Shakespeare work, died on 11 July 1989?

2. How much did the world's first PC cost when launched by IBM on 12 August 1981: $565, $1,565 or $2,565?

3. Which Madonna track, taken from an album containing controversial religious imagery, hit number 1 in the United Kingdom, United States, Sweden, Switzerland, Norway, Poland, Ireland, New Zealand and Australia in 1989?

4. Which Swedish group released Look Sharp in 1988, an album featuring the tracks Dressed for Success, The Look and Listen to Your Heart?

5. Who dressed as Donald Duck for the encore to a free concert in New York's Central Park on 13 September 1980?

6. Which DX was the leader of China from 1982 until 1987?

7. What is the name of the young girl played by Drew Barrymore in the 1982 movie, ET: Georgia, Gaby or Gertie?

8. Which country's high speed train service, the TGV, commenced operation on 27 September 1981?

9. Matt Smith was born in Northampton, UK, in 1982 and went on to play which incarnation of Time Lord Doctor Who, for which he received a Bafta Award nomination in 2011: the ninth, tenth or eleventh?

10. In the 1989 film Shirley Valentine, the lead character fled from Liverpool to... where?

Quiz 4

1. Under which name is actor Lawrence Tureaud, usually billed?

2. How many times did Nasa launch one or other of its Space Shuttles in 1985: once, four times, nine times, fifteen times?

3. Which TS was the site of protests in China in 1989?

4. Which Australian actor, born in 1983, went on to play Thor in the 2011 film of the same name?

5. Steffi Graf and Boris Becker won the two singles' finals at the 1989 Wimbledon Championships. Which country did they both represent?

6. Which computer, the first of a long line, went on sale in January 1984 bundled with two applications called MacDraw and MacWrite?

7. What breed of dog was Cujo in the 1983 film based on Stephen King's book of the same name?

8. How many episodes of The Golden Girls were made in total? 80, 180, 280 or 380?

9. When Price Andrew and Sarah Ferguson married in London on 23 July 1986, was it at St Paul's Cathedral, Westminster Abbey or Windsor Castle?

10. Approximately how many people were there on Earth at the start of the 1980s? 4.5bn, 5.5bn or 6.5bn?

Quiz 5

1. In which year was Michael Jackson's Thriller released, which eventually became the best-selling album of all time?

2. Who became the seventh actor to play Doctor Who on 7 September 1987?

3. Did actor Ray Bolger, who died in January 1987, play the lion, scarecrow or tin man in The Wizard of Oz?

4. Who won the 1986 FIFA World Cup? Mexico, Argentina, West Germany or France?

5. English actor Bernard Lee died in 1981. Which character did he play in the James Bond film series?

6. US tennis player Andy Roddick, born in August 1982, won the mens' final at Wimbledon in two consecutive years. Were they 2002 and 2003, 2003 and 2004 or 2004 and 2005?

7. Breakfast TV launched in Britain on 17 January (on the BBC) and 1 February (on commercial channels), in which year? 1981, 1982, 1983 or 1984?

8. Which US police series created by Steven Bochco and Michael Kozoll, ran from 1981 until 1987, comprising 146 episodes in total?

9. Which American motor manufacturer took over British carmaker Jaguar in November 1989?

10. The name Hannibal was just a nickname for one of the A-Team characters. What was that character's "real" name in the series?

Quiz 6

1. What day of the week was the first day of 1980?

2. Where were the 1984 Summer Olympics staged?

3. Which comic actor, famed for his portrayal of Sergeant Ernest Bilko, died in November 1985?

4. Who wrote the soundtrack for ET: The Extra-Terrestrial?

5. True or false: Stephen Hawking appeared in Star Trek: The Next Generation?

6. Who founded Scientology, and died on 24 January 1986?

7. What is Christine, as featured in the title of Stephen King's 1983 book?

8. In which year did Argentina and the United Kingdom fight over ownership of the Falkland Islands?

9. Which German architect of the Nazi era died on 1 September 1981?

10. Shares in which software giant went on sale for the first time on 14 March 1986: Microsoft, Atari, Apple or Commodore?

Quiz 7

1. Which special envoy to the Archbishop of Canterbury was kidnapped in Beirut in 1987 and held until 1991?

2. Which TV series about a talking car and its driver came to an end in 1986?

3. Which American actor, later married to Angelina Jolie, made his film debut in 1987's No Man's Land?

4. With which single did Madonna make her debut on 6 October 1982?

5. Which 1988 cult classic starring Sonny Bono, Debbie Harry, Divine and Ricki Lake was set in 1962-era Baltimore?

6. Which AS was the Egyptian president assassinated in Cairo in 1981?

7. Beverley Hills Cop was nominated for Best Original Screenplay at 1984's Academy Awards. Did it win?

8. Who released her third album, True Blue, in 1986?

9. By what name is 1984-born singer Katheryn Elizabeth Hudson better known?

10. In which far eastern city did Disney open a new Disneyland theme park on 10 April 1983?

Quiz 8

1. Which British-American actor, known for his roles in North by Northwest, Suspicion, Bringing Up Baby and The Philadelphia story, died in November 1986?

2. Back to the Future and which other Michael J Fox film were released on home video in 1986?

3. Which 1986 cinema release starred Tom Cruise, Kelly McGillis, Val Kilmer, Anthony Edwards and Tom Skerritt?

4. Margaret Thatcher won two elections during the 1980s: the first in 1983 and the second... when?

5. The James Bond film series marked its 25th year in 1987 by releasing its 15th installment. What was it called?

6. Whose three-year marriage to sound engineer Renate Blauel began with a Valentines Day 1984 wedding?

7. Which artist, famed for saying that everyone would be famous for 15 minutes, died in New York on 22 February 1987?

8. Which French musician released the album Rendez-Vous in 1986?

9. Which long-running TV series, featuring the Georgia-based Duke family, came to an end in 1985 after airing 147 episodes?

10. Who wrote the book on which Stanley Kubrick's 1980 movie, The Shining, was based?

Quiz 9

1. In which US state did British entrepreneur Richard Noble set a new land speed record of 633mph while driving Thrust 2 on 4 October 1983?
2. Who presented the first episode of her long-running television discussion programme on 8 September 1986?
3. Which US volcano erupted on 18 May 1980, killing 57 and causing $3bn of damage?
4. How many Oscar nominations did 1988 film Rain Man receive? Four, six, eight or ten?
5. In which year did the US Air Force unveil its "invisible" stealth aircraft, the F-117A? 1984, 1986 or 1988?
6. Which Arnold Schwarzenegger film is set in May 1984?
7. Which model and actress, who played Vesper, the female lead in the Bond film Casino Royale, was born on 5 July 1980?
8. Which film won best picture at the 1982 Academy Awards: Chariots of Fire, On Golden Pond or Raiders of the Lost Ark?
9. Whose first solo single release, Never Gonna Give You Up, was released on new year's day 1987?
10. What was the nationality of architect and designed Erno Goldfinger, who died in London in November 1987?

Quiz 10

1. Which earned more at the US box office in 1985: Back to the Future, Out of Africa or The Goonies?
2. When written in Roman numerals, which year of the 1980s had the most digits in the whole century?
3. Which actress, which the lyrics of the Madonna song Vogue claimed "gave good face", died in May 1987?

4. Who performed the song Let The River Run in the 1988 film Working Girl?

5. Which landmark game was released by Nintendo on 9 July 1981?

6. Name the German-Austrian actor who died in 1982, five years after playing Carl Stromberg, the villain in the Bond film, The Spy Who Loved Me.

7. Which Susan Hill ghost story, published in 1983, has since been made into a 1989 TV film, a 2012 cinema film, and is also the second-longest running play in London's West End after Agatha Christie's The Mousetrap?

8. Which Canadian telecoms company, famed for its BlackBerry handsets, was established in 1984?

9. Which British prime minister won a landslide re-election on 9 June 1983 following her successful re-taking of the Falkland Islands the previous year?

10. Who starred opposite Patrick Swayze in the 1987 film Dirty Dancing?

Quiz 11

1. Which incarnation of Doctor Who was played by Patrick Troughton, who died in March 1987? The first, second or third?

2. On which island was Man of Steel actor Henry Cavill born on 5 May 1983?

3. For which film, in which she plays a wife who goes on holiday without her husband, did Pauline Collins win 1989's BAFTA for Best Actress?

4. David A Kennedy, who died aged 28 on 25 April 1984, was whose son? US president John F Kennedy or US attorney general Robert F Kennedy?

5. Who was elected the first socialist president of France on 21 May 1981?

6. True or false: Carrie Fisher played a part in the 1980 John Belushi film, The Blue Brothers?

7. Which Irish footballer was born on 8 July 1980?

8. Which two-part 1983 miniseries depicted aliens invading earth in a fleet of 50 flying saucers?

9. Which virus did American researchers announce the discovery of on 23 April 1984?

10. In which city did a fire in the underground railway system kill 31 and injure 100 people?

Quiz 12

1. How many series were made of US TV show Knight Rider?

2. Name the British artist, best known for his semi-abstract bronze sculptures, who died on 31 August 1986.

3. Did British Airways employ its first female pilots in 1980, 1984 or 1987?

4. Where did Disney announce in 1987 that it was going to build a new theme park?

5. In which year did prime minister Margaret Thatcher survive an assassination attempt when a Brighton hotel she was staying in was bombed?

6. Iceland ended a 74-year-long prohibition of what on 1 March 1989? Beer, prostitution or cigarettes?

7. Where did Swedish actress Ingrid Bergman died, aged 67, in August 1982: London, Stockholm, Berlin or Vienna?

8. In which civil rights leader's honour did president Ronald Reagan sign a 1983 bill declaring that the third Monday of every January should be a public holiday? The first holiday was implemented in 1986.

9. Which English novelist, author of Jamaica Inn and Rebecca, died in Fowey, Cornwall, on 19 April 1989?

10. What nationality was Mehmet Ali Agca, who shot Pope John Paul II in St Peter's Square in 1981?

Quiz 13

1. Who wrote the 1989 book, The Russia House?
2. Complete the name of the 1988 single taken from Michael Jackson's album, Bad: Man In The... what?
3. Which military alliance celebrated its 40th anniversary on 4 April 1989?
4. Whose first solo single hit number 1 in the 1984 singles charts of the United Kingdom, United States, Canada, Netherlands, Switzerland, Poland, Ireland and Australia?
5. Which English actor, known for his Shakespearean work, made his film debut in 1987's A Month in the Country?
6. Guion Bluford became the first African-American to do what on 30 August 1983?
7. Which British accountant's 44 chapter book, The Easy Way to Stop Smoking, was a breakthrough success in 1985?
8. Which great-granddaughter of a hotel chain's founder was born on 17 February 1981?
9. Which future star of Top Gun appeared in his first film in 1981?
10. Which 1989 film starring Jessica Tandy won the following year's Academy Award for Best Picture?

Quiz 14

1. Who shot Ronald Reagan outside a hotel in Washington DC on 30 March 1981?
2. Name the comedy mystery TV series that debuted in 1985, starring Cybill Shepherd and Bruce Willis as private detectives.
3. What was the nationality of Sophie, the immigrant, titular character of the 1982 Meryl Streep film, Sophie's Choice: Polish, Danish or Irish?

4. What was the name of the car in The Dukes of Hazard?

5. Was the 1987 British-Italian film The Last Emperor set in China, India or Japan?

6. Who bit off the head of a live bat that had been thrown at him during a 1982 concert in Des Moines, Iowa, when he thought it was made of rubber?

7. Which description of young business people was coined by Dan Rottenberg on 1 May 1980?

8. Name the character played by Richard Dean Anderson in the 1980s TV show about a secret agent come troubleshooter who works for the US Department of External Services.

9. British actor Ben Wishaw was born in October 1980 and later went on to play which iconic character in the James Bond film series?

10. Who won an Academy Award for Best Original Song for Top Gun's Take My Breath Away?

Quiz 15

1. Which legendary John Carpenter horror, starring Jamie Lee Curtis, hit cinemas on 1 February 1980?

2. The first American woman in space blasted off on the Space Shuttle Challenger on 18 June 1983. What was her name?

3. In which month of 1984 was The Empire Strikes Back first released on home video?

4. Which computer game, featuring four ghosts and a happy hungry character, debuted in Japan on 22 May 1980?

5. Which future member of The A Team made his acting debut in 1982's Rocky III?

6. Which TG was a 1987 film starring Tom Cruise and Kelly McGillis?

7. Where were the summer Olympic Games of 1980 held?

8. Which Bond film first appeared in cinemas in 1981?

9. Who was pope at the start of the 1980s?

10. For which infection did the US Food and Drug Administration start screening donated blood on 4 March 1985?

Quiz 16

1. Terry Pratchett published the first instalment of his Discworld novel series in 1983. What was that first book called?

2. Which Egyptian-style building opened at Paris' Louvre museum in March 1989?

3. Which singer died in 1983, aged 32, of heart failure caused by complications related to anorexia nervosa?

4. How many bullets hit Pope John Paul II during a May 1981 assassination attempt?

5. The dictator of which East European country was executed alongside his wife on Christmas day 1989?

6. When was the Internet Domain Name System (the central directory of sites) created?

7. Which long-running Middle Eastern war came to an end on 20 August 1988?

8. How old was 1986-born Jamie Bell when he first appeared in cinemas in the title role of the film Billy Elliot?

9. Which 1987 movie starring Michael Douglas and Glenn Close featured a now infamous scene depicting the boiling of a pet rabbit?

10. How many episodes were there in the original 1983 sci-fi drama series, V: 2, 12 or 22?

Quiz 17

1. What was the recommended selling price of the DeLorean DMC-12 car, which featured in Back to the Future, upon its release in 1981? $25,000; $50,000 or $75,000?

2. Which iconic game was released for the Nintendo Entertainment System on 13 September 1985?

3. John Lennon was killed outside his apartment in which city in December 1980?

4. Was Filoli, a 16 acre country estate and house built in 1915, used as the home of the Carringtons in Dynasty, Ewings in Dallas or Channings in Falcon Crest?

5. By what name is 1987-born singer Joscelyn Eve Stoker better known?

6. For how many years did the Space Shuttle fleet remain in service after the first orbital test flights of 1981?

7. How many runners took part in the first London Marathon, in March 1981?

8. What kind of adventure did Bill and Ted have, according to the title of the 1989 film?

9. Who won 1983's Golden Globe for Best Actress in a Drama Series: Joan Collins, Linda Evans, Jane Wyman or Stefanie Powers?

10. Who wrote the play Educating Rita, which debuted on stage in 1980 and was later adapted for film?

Quiz 18

1. Laszlo Biro, who died in 1985, is famous for having invented which everyday office product?

2. Name the 1980 film starring John Hurt and Anthony Hopkins, and directed by David Lynch, which depicted the life of Joseph Merrick.

3. Which 1985 kids' comedy film featured the characters Mikey, Brand, Data, Mouth and Chunk?

4. Which British actor, who found fame in Queer as Folk and went on to star as Jackson Teller in Sons of Anarchy, was born on 19 April 1980?

5. The prime ministers of which two Scandinavian countries died in 1986?

6. Who took over from Peter Davison in the role of Doctor Who on 16 March 1984?

7. Which comedian, of Blues Brothers fame, was found dead from an apparent drug overdose, in a Los Angeles hotel on 5 March 1982?

8. Four streets in which British city were named after the four members of the Beatles on 18 August 1982?

9. The Empire Strikes Back and 9 to 5 were the two top-grossing films at the US box office in 1980. Which took the number one spot?

10. Which film won the Academy Awards for Best Picture, Best Director, Best Actress and Best Supporting Actor in 1983: Educating Rita, Flashdance, Terms of Endearment or WarGames?

Quiz 19

1. Who starred as Raymond Babbit in the 1988 film Rain Man?

2. Which Bond film was the sixth highest grossing film at 1983's US box office?

3. By what title was Tenzin Gyatso, recipient of the 1989 Nobel Prize for Peace, better known?

4. Who won the Best Supporting Actor Academy Award in 1988 for playing Jim Malone in The Untouchables?

5. What was the name of the talking car in TV series, Knight Rider?

6. Which actor, known for her portrayal of Sarah Connor in The Terminator series of films, debuted on cinema screens in 1982's TAG The Assassination Game?

7. Who released the album Slippery When Wet in 1986?

8. What was the name of the Detroit police officer played by Eddie Murphy in the 1984 film Beverly Hills Cop?

9. How many years had Elizabeth II been on the throne by the start of 1986?

10. In which year was Ronald Reagan sworn in as 40th president of the United States?

Quiz 20

1. Which 82 year old British author wrote 23 romantic novels during 1983 alone?

2. Which Jamaican singer died from cancer, aged 36, on 11 May 1981?

3. Who played oil magnate Blake Carrington in US TV drama Dynasty?

4. Of which country was Kil Il-sung the leader throughout the 1980s? North Korea, South Korea, Cambodia or China?

5. A Boeing 747 set a new round the world record on 30 January 1988. Did it take 36 hours, 46 hours or 56 hours to complete the lap?

6. How old was athlete Jesse Owens when he died at the end of March 1980?

7. What nationality was rock band Europe, which released the album The Final Countdown in 1986?

8. Who played Max Zorrin in the 1985 Bond film A View to a Kill?

9. Which South African won the Nobel Price for Peace in 1984?

10. During which country's Grand Prix race was racing driver Gilles Villeneuve killed on 8 May 1982?

Quiz 21

1. Which prime minister survived an assassination attempt when her hotel was bombed by the Privisional Irish Republican Army on 12 October 1984?

2. Which American band, whose name is a three-letter acronym, made its TV debut on 6 October 1983's episode of Late Night with David Letterman?

3. How many Academy Awards did Out of Africa win at the 1986 ceremony? Seven, eight or nine?

4. Which architecturally important, inside-out building designed by Richard Rogers, opened in London on 18 November 1984?

5. Which mercurial businessman introduced the world to the first Apple Macintosh in January 1984?

6. Complete the name of the 1980 Disney movie: Herbie Goes _____

7. Which English-American author of A Single Man, whose Berlin Stories was adapted for the stage as Cabaret, died in 1986, aged 81?

8. Name the 1986 film directed by Jim Henson, executive produced by George Lucas and starring David Bowie.

9. After which far eastern country was the British band that released a 1980 album called Gentleman Take Polaroids named?

10. Did Fame or The Empire Strikes Back win the Oscar for Best Original Score in 1981?

Quiz 22

1. Who did Lady Diana Spencer marry on 29 July 1981?

2. Who played Captain Jean-Luc Picard in Star Trek: The Next Generation?

3. The first version of which image editing software was developed in 1987 and released the following year?

4. What is 1985 in Roman numerals?

5. Which highly appropriate great-grandson received the world's first commercial mobile telephone call?

6. Which musician, known as the King of Swing, died on 13 June 1986?

7. Kian Egan, born on 29 April 1980, was a member of one of the biggest pop bands ever to come from Ireland, but was it Westlife or Boyzone?

8. Was the 1986 football World Cup held in Mexico, Brazil or Argentina?

9. Which actor, who died in 1986, was famed for the catchphrase "You Dirty Rat", despite never actually saying it in any film?

10. Which far eastern ruler, who assumed office in 2011, aged 27, was born in 1984?

Quiz 23

1. Who played James Bond in the 1989 film Licence to Kill?

2. Which British actress, who went on to play Lady Rose Aldridge in Downton Abbey, was born in April 1989?

3. Composer and Lyricist Irving Berlin died in New York in 1989, but in which country was he born 101 years earlier?

4. Which country singer starred in the 1980 film, 9 to 5?

5. Whose Virgin tour opened in New York on 10 April 1985?

6. The Soviet Union started to build the Mir space station in 1986. When did it complete it? The same year, in five years, or in ten years?

7. Which two clay-based characters debuted in the 1989 stop-motion film A Grand Day Out?

8. From which spaceport did Challenger lift off before exploding 73 seconds into its 1986 flight?

9. Name the Indian prime minister assassinated by two of his security guards in 1984.

10. Which former Star Trek actor directed the 1987 movie, Three Men and a Baby?

Quiz 24

1. How many episodes were made of US TV show Knight Rider: 90, 190 or 290?

2. In which city did the Churchill War Rooms museum first open for business in 1984?

3. How many Academy Awards did The Last Emperor win in 1988? None, one, six or nine?

4. When did the BBC comedy, Only Fools and Horses, debut?

5. Did 1988 film Rain Man win a quarter, half or all of the eight Academy Awards for which it was nominated?

6. Who ran against George HW Bush in the US presidential election of 1988?

7. Heinz Linge, who died in 1980, might never have come to prominence had he not been appointed personal valet to a more notorious man. Who was that man?

8. The Color of Money and The Color Purple were both released on home video in which year?

9. How many of the 50 US states did Ronald Reagan win in the 1984 US presidential election?

10. Which Broadway musical about an orphan was adapted for cinema in 1982?

Quiz 25

1. Which broadcasting organisation released a series of 8-bit home computers between 1981 and 1994, which became standard in British schools but were less successful when introduced to the US?

2. In which 1988 film did Sigourney Weaver play naturalist Dian Fossey?

3. The Soviet Union space shuttle, Buran, made its maiden flight on 15 November 1988. How many more flights would it make before the programme was terminated?

4. Where did Space Shuttle Columbia land at the end of the first ever orbit of a Space Shuttle, in April 1981?

5. Which four-wheel-drive Audi was launched in West Germany on 3 March 1980?

6. Which 1986 comedy, starring Paul Hogan, was Australia's highest-grossing film until 2015?

7. By what name is the B-2 Spirit aircraft, which took its first flight in July 1989, better known?

8. Who played a streetwise girl accused of murdering her boyfriend in the 1987 comedy Who's That Girl?

9. Terry Pratchett's The Light Fantastic, published in 1986, was the second book in his series set... where?

10. Which union leader and future president of Poland instigated a series of landmark strikes in the Gdansk Shipyard between 7 and 31 August 1980?

Quiz 26

1. How many leap years were there in the 1980s?

2. How many Bond films debuted in the 1980s: 1, 3, 5 or 7?

3. Which superhero did 1983-born Henry Cavill play in the movie Man of Steel?

4. Which female actor, born in April 1982, has starred in 2004's Wimbledon, the second season of television's Fargo, and Sci-fi rom-com Eternal Sunshine of the Spotless Mind?

5. In which country was tennis player Maria Sharapova born on 19 April 1987?

6. Which US president's twin daughters, Jenna and Barbara, were born on 25 November 1981?

7. In which year did German war film Das Boot enjoy worldwide success upon its cinema release?

8. Which US TV comedy's theme song was Thank You For Being A Friend?

9. Which 1987-born actor played Troy Bolton in High School Musical films 1, 2 and 3?

10. Which aircraft did Boeing announce it was to stop producing on 1 February 1983: 727, 747 or 767?

Quiz 27

1. How many episodes made up Knight Rider's original four-season run from 1982 to 1986: 60, 90, 120 or 150?

2. Who won the 1981 Oscar for Best Actor: Jack Lemon, John Hurt, Peter O'Toole or Robert De Niro?

3. Which Irish supergroup made its first US TV appearance on the Tomorrow show on 4 June 1982?

4. Which actor and dancer, born Frederick Austerlitz, died in June 1987, aged 88?

5. Which Caribbean island nation did 7300 United States troops invade on 25 October 1983?

6. Which power station went into meltdown on 26 April 1986?

7. What was the name of the young buy who discovered ET in the film of the same name?

8. Which 1986-born British actress went on to play the part of agent Strawberry Fields in the Bond film Quantum of Solace?

9. What is the name of the country in which George Orwell's book 1984 is set?

10. Which WFRR was a groundbreaking 1988 film starring Bob Hoskins and Christoper Lloyd, which is notable for the way in which is combined live action and animation?

Quiz 28

1. What was the significance of the film title My Left Foot?
2. True or false: Pamela Anderson, who played CJ Parker, appeared in every episode from its 1989 debut until its 2001 termination?
3. Under which name did Windows 3.1 bundle the game Klondike, in which players sort seven piles of cards into their four suits?
4. Who was US president at the end of the 1980s?
5. Who played the first wife of Blake Carrington in the TV series Dynasty?
6. The first Inspector Rebus novel, Knots and Crosses, was published in 1987. Who wrote it?
7. The soundtrack album for which David Bowie film was first released in October 1983?
8. Which global superpower boycotted the 1984 Summer Olympics?
9. The author of The Guns of Navarone, Where Eagles Dare and Ice Station Zebra died in 1987. Who was he?
10. Where was singer Charlotte Church born in February 1986? Swansea, Llandudno, Cardiff or Prestatyn?

Quiz 29

1. Videodisc and Laserdisc both debuted in 1981. Which came first?
2. How old was 1983-born singer and songwriter Amy Winehouse when she died of alcohol poisoning in Camden, London.
3. Name the 1980 Roald Dahl book, with the initials TT.
4. George Gallup, who died in 1984, was renowned for his work in measuring what?

5. Which European nation's queen abdicated on 30 April 1980, handing power to her daughter Beatrix?

6. For how many seasons did Little House on the Prairie run before coming to an end in 1983: 9, 10, 11 or 12?

7. Which British prime minister visited Berlin one day after the fall of the Berlin wall on 10 November 1989?

8. What was the name of the captain in Star Trek: The Next Generation upon its debut at the end of the 1980s?

9. Which actor, who went on to play Frodo Baggins in the Lord of the Rings trilogy, made his cinema debut in 1989's Back to the Future Part II?

10. Which novelist published his debut novel, The Hunt for Red October, in 1984?

Quiz 30

1. In 1981, the Centers for Disease Control coined the term "4H Disease" to describe a newly-detected illness that primarily affected heroin users, homosexuals, hemophiliacs and Haitians. By what name is it better known now?

2. Who directed the 1980s' biggest box-office hit, ET: The Extra-Terrestrial?

3. What was the name of the distinctive dance method first demonstrated by Michael Jackson during a performance of Billie Jean on 25 March 1983?

4. Of what was a hat-wearing jalapeno pepper called Pique the mascot, from May until June 1986?

5. Roger Moore stepped down from the role of James Bond in 1985. Who was announced as his replacement?

6. In which coastal city did Margaret Thatcher survive a 1984 assassination attempt?

7. Who scored the most goals in the 1986 FIFA World Cup? Diego Maradonna, Gary Lineker or Enzo Scifo?

8. Which manufacturer launched the Escort Mk3 car in Europe on 2 September 1980?

9. Which Rocky film was released in 1982: Rocky, Rocky II or Rocky III?

10. When, in 1989, was the Berlin Wall breached? 9 September, 9 October, 9 November or 9 December?

Quiz 31

1. Joanne Froggatt, born on 23 August 1980, went on to play Anna Bates in which British period drama?

2. Who released an album called Bad on 31 August 1987?

3. From which company did Steve Jobs resign on 13 September 1985?

4. When was the videodisc introduced by RCA: 1980, 1981, 1982 or 1983?

5. With which planet in our solar system did the space probe Voyager 2 make its first encounter on 24 January 1986?

6. Which 1988-born English princess is the eldest daughter of Andrew and Sarah, the Duke and Duchess of York: Beatrice or Eugenie?

7. Which country won the most medals at the 1988 Summer Olympics in Seoul: the Soviet Union, East Germany, the United States or South Korea?

8. True or false: 9 to 5 was Dolly Parton's second film role?

9. Who performed Eye of the Tiger, the theme to the 1982 Sylvester Stallone movie, Rocky III?

10. For which of the following did Out of Africa NOT win an Academy Award in 1986: Best Picture, Best Director, Best Original Screenplay, Best Adapted Screenplay?

Quiz 32

1.   What did Ronald Reagan call on Soviet premier Mikhael Gorbachev to "tear down" during a visit to Germany in 1987?

2.   Who starred as stuntman Colt Seavers in The Fall Guy from 1981 until 1986?

3.   The former CEO of which motor company, and grandson of the founder from whom the company got its name, died in September 1987?

4.   Under what name was Dick King-Smith's 1983 book The Sheep-Pig adapted for cinema?

5.   Which four-members of a Swedish pop group made their final appearance together on 11 December 1982, on British TV's Late, Late Breakfast Show?

6.   Which R&B and soul singer was born in Sunderland, Tyne and Wear, on 10 March 1987?

7.   Advertising director Peter Mayle published a book about his first year of living in which part of the world in 1989?

8.   Colonel Harland David Sanders, who died in December 1980, is best known for founding which fast food restaurant chain?

9.   Two Ian Fleming stories were released to cinemas in 1981. One was For Your Eyes Only. What was the other?

10. Name the Gary Larson comic strip, which debuted in the San Francisco Chronicle on 1 January 1980.

Quiz 33

1.   GRID, standing for gay-related immune deficiency was an early name for which infectious disease?

2.   Shares in which airline went on sale in 1987? British Airways, American Airlines, Quantas or Air France?

3. In which year did Mikhail Gorbachev become leader of the Soviet Union?

4. Complete the sequence: Hannibal, Face, Murdock and...

5. The first model in which iconic line of computers did Apple introduce on 24 January 1984?

6. Who won the Best Actress Oscar in 1981: Goldie Hawn, Sissy Spacek or Mary Tyler Moore?

7. Which 1987 book by Roddy Doyle told the story of a group of unemployed people in Dublin who formed a soul band?

8. In which year was the first permanent Internet link between the United States and Europe established?

9. Which Portuguese footballer was born on 5 February 1985?

10. Which 1982-born British actor has played Stephen Hawking in The Theory of Everything, Lili Elbe in The Danish Girl and Newt Scamander in Fantastic Beasts and Where to Find Them?

Quiz 34

1. Which 1982 film starred Dustin Hoffman, who was backed up by Jessica Lange and Bill Murray, introduced Geena Davis in her cinema debut and was directed by Sydney Pollack?

2. Which of the Space Shuttles began its maiden voyage on 30 August 1984?

3. Which four-part miniseries starring Richard Chamberlain, Barbara Stanwyck and Christopher Plummer, broadcast originally in March 1983, was based on a book of the same name by Colleen McCullough?

4. Who played the selfish, spoiled heiress Joanna Stayton in the 1987 film Overboard?

5. Which former US president's daughter, Chelsea, was born on 27 February 1980?

6. Who was the most famous creation of Herge, the Belgian cartoonist who died on 3 March 1983?

7. Where did Pope John Paul II survive an assassination attempt on 13 May 1981?

8. Who sang (I've Had) The Time of My Life for the film Dirty Dancing?

9. In which year of the 1980s is the 1996 Cohen brothers film Fargo set?

10. In which city was Kelly Osbourne born on 27 October 1984?

Quiz 35

1. Who was elected president of United States in 1980?

2. What did the albums released by Bryan Adams, Orchestral Manoeuvres in the Dark, Survivor, Peter Gabriel, and Iron Maiden, all from 1980, have in common?

3. Complete the 1985 film title – Star Trek III: The Search for...

4. NASA scientist James Hansen testified to the US Senate on 23 June 1988 that which manmade phenomena was now affecting the planet?

5. Which OOA was a 1985 epic movie directed by Sydney Pollack, starring Robert Redford and Meryl Streep?

6. Was 1986 designated the international year of peace, women or children by the United Nations?

7. Which actress, who played the female lead character, Laura Jesson, in Brief Encounter, died on 26 April 1982?

8. On which day of 1980 was tennis player Venus Williams born: 17 April, 17 May or 17 June?

9. Complete the title of Ken Follett's 1989 book: The Pillars of... what?

10. The first commercial internet domain was registered on 15 March 1985, but was it apple.com, microsoft.com, symbolics.com or ford.com?

Quiz 36

1. Which company released the world's first ever auto-focus SLR camera on 20 February 1985?
2. In which year did Ronald Reagan survive being shot in the chest during an assassination attempt?
3. What was Blue Thunder in the 1983 film and 1984 television series of the same name?
4. How many countries boycotted the 1980 Summer Olympics in Moscow? 5, 35, 65 or 105?
5. In which country was US TV sitcom M*A*S*H set?
6. 1980 spanned two years of the Ethiopian calendar. Were they 1952 and 1953, 1962 and 1963 or 1972 and 1973?
7. The 1984 Winter Olympics took place in Sarajevo, which was in which former country?
8. True or false: Frasier star Kelsey Grammer appeared in Star Trek: The Next Generation?
9. Which Tim Rice and Andrew Lloyd Webber musical, set in South America, won the 1981 Grammy Award for Best Cast Show Album?
10. The United States' first ever CD manufacturing plant opened on 21 September 1984. Which American artist's album was the first to roll off the production line?

Quiz 37

1. Which director, also responsible for Blade Runner, directed Apple's 1984 commercial for the first Macintosh computer?
2. Who was sworn in as US President on 20 January 1989?
3. Katharine Hepburn, Susan Sarandon, Meryl Streep and Diane Keaton were all nominated for the Best Actress at 1982's Academy Awards. Who won?

4. Who starred as the title characters in 1980s police series Cagney and Lacey?

5. Which book by Jeffrey Archer, originally published the year before, reached number one on the New York Times best-seller list in 1980?

6. Which Lionel Richie song won the Academy Award for Best Original Song in 1986?

7. Which ROTLA, released in 1981, was the first story in a period adventure series starring Harrison Ford?

8. Who took the lead in 1988 film Big?

9. Which Egyptian president was assassinated during an army parade on 6 October 1981?

10. What was painted on the roof of General Lee, the car in the Dukes of Hazard?

Quiz 38

1. How many terrorists laid siege to the Iranian Embassy in London in April and May 1980?

2. Which action-film actor released his album, The Return of Bruno, in January 1987?

3. Name the county police commissioner who spent his life chasing the Duke boys in The Dukes of Hazard.

4. Which famous couple married at Westminster Abbey on 23 July 1986?

5. Which landmark film by Ridley Scott, starring Harrison Ford and Rutger Hauer, was a 1982 adaptation of the book Do Androids Dream of Electric Sheep by Philip K Dick?

6. What was the biggest box office hit of the 1980s?

7. What was the name of Madonna's second studio album, released in November 1984?

8. True or false: Tom Hanks made his cinema debut in 1980 in a film called He Knows You're Alone?

9. Which musical by ABBA's Benny Andersson and Björn Ulvaeus opened on New York's Broadway in 1988 and closed 65 performances later?

10. Which voice actor, who provided the voices for Bugs Bunny, Daffy Duck, Barney Rubble and others, died on 10 July 1989?

Quiz 39

1. In which year was the Turner Art Prize first awarded?

2. Of what did scientists of the British Antarctic Survey announce the discovery on 16 May 1985?

3. Where was Olympic gold medallist Usain Bolt born in August 1986?

4. What was the first name of the titular character in Goldie Hawn's 1980s comedy, Private Benjamin?

5. Whoopie Goldberg was nominated for the Academy Award for best actress at the 1986 ceremony. For which film?

6. Which entrepreneur broke the speed record for crossing the Atlantic in a boat in June 1986?

7. Which British band released A New Flame, its third album, in February 1989?

8. The horn in General Lee, the car in the Dukes of Hazard, played how many notes of the song Dixie when pressed?

9. Two types of precious stone were used in the £30,000 engagement ring given to Lady Diana Spencer by Prince Charles in February 1981. Which ones?

10. Which two cities hosted winter Olympics games in the 1980s?

Quiz 40

1. Which landmark sci-fi sequel was released on 21 May 1980?
2. What was the name of Max Zorin's sidekick in the Bond film A View to a Kill, played by Grace Jones?
3. What role on the crew of the Enterprise did Deanna Troi fulfil in Star Trek: The Next Generation?
4. When did the BBC broadcast the first episode of its long-running soap, EastEnders?
5. How many years after their 1981 marriage did Prince Charles and Princess Diana separate?
6. Which sci-fi movie, released on 9 July, was the first feature film to extensively use computer animation?
7. On what day of the week was Christmas day 1980?
8. Which George Michael song was 1988's best-selling single in the US?
9. Which actress, born in 1985, starred as Elizabeth Swann in the Pirates of the Caribbean film series?
10. Which US TV personality, with the initials KK, was born on 21 October 1980?

Quiz 41

1. Which Canadian city hosted the 1988 Winter Olympics?
2. In which middle-Eastern city was actress Natalie Portman born in 1981?
3. Which Star Wars film debuted in 1983? Return of the Jedi, Revenge of the Sith, or The Empire Strikes Back?
4. Which iconic spacecraft made its first orbital flight from 12 to 14 April 1981?
5. True or false: Michael J Fox's first film was 1980's Midnight Madness?

6. Why did the Osborne 1 mark a worldwide computing first upon its release on 3 April 1981?

7. Which American drama about the super rich ran from 1981 until 1989? Dallas, Dynasty, Knotts Landing or Falcon Crest?

8. For how many days was Ronald Reagan hospitalised as a result of a 1981 assassination attempt?

9. What was remarkable about the first Apple Macintosh when it went on sale in January 1984?

10. Which 1987 comedy starred Robin Williams as a DJ on the Armed Forces Radio Service in Vietnam?

Quiz 42

1. Which British actor, who died in 1982, was best known for his depiction of Captain Mainwaring in the long-running sitcom Dad's Army?

2. Which Canadian entertainment company, best known for its extravagant travelling circuses, was founded on 16 June 1984?

3. In which year did George Orwell publish the book 1984?

4. Which of these 1982 films was released first: Star Trek II The Wrath of Khan, Grease 2 or Airplane II?

5. Which was the last year to include an L when written in Roman numerals, until 2040?

6. Which film won the 1988 Academy Award for Best Original Screenplay? Moonstruck, The Last Emperor, Fatal Attraction or Full Metal Jacket?

7. How many "General Lee" cars were made for the filming of The Dukes of Hazard? 25, 125, 225 or 325?

8. Who went home with the Oscar for Best Director in 1982? Warren Beatty or Steven Spielberg?

9. Complete the title of the 1989 film directed by Steven Sonderberg: Sex, Lies and... what?

10. In which game, originally released on the ZX Spectrum in 1983 but eventually migrating to Windows, GameBoy Commodore and others, did you guide a character called Willy around a series of 20 underground caverns?

Quiz 43

1. Which singer, famous for performing Only the Lonely and Oh, Pretty Woman, died of a heart attack, aged 52, on 6 December 1988?
2. Who beat West Germany to win the 1982 FIFA World Cup?
3. How many episodes of the A-Team were broadcast between it debuting in 1983 and going off air in 1987: 98, 198 or 298?
4. How many episodes of the US comedy TV show Moonlighting were made, following its debut in 1985: 44, 55, 66 or 77?
5. Who played James Bond in the 1981 film, For Your Eyes Only?
6. Which film depicted a period in the life of Maria von Trapp, who died in March 1987?
7. What was Street Hawk in the TV series of the same name?
8. The film ET had a budget of $10.5m. How much of that was spent on the ET model itself?
9. Which future Lois Lane, Bond girl and Desperate Housewife made her cinema debut in 1989's The Big Picture?
10. Why was Atlantis in the news on 3 October 1985?

Quiz 44

1. Which group released its album, The Joshua Tree, in 1987?
2. Before being elected president of Czechoslovakia in 1989, what was Vaclav Havel's profession?

3. Which long-running sci-fi series did the BBC cancel after 26 years on 6 December 1989?

4. Which future James Bond actor made his cinema debut with 1980's The Long Good Friday?

5. Elijah Wood was born in January 1981, and went on to play which character in the Lord of the Rings film trilogy?

6. Which animation studio, later acquired by Disney, was founded in California on 3 February 1986?

7. Which car did Ford launch in Europe on 13 October 1982 to replace the UK's Cortina and continental Europe's Taunus?

8. When was Stephen Hawking's landmark book, A Brief History of Time, published?

9. When John Hinckley Jr tried to assassinate president Ronald Reagan in March 1981, he failed, but he did paralyse the president's press secretary, James Brady. Brady eventually died of his wounds, how many years later: 3, 13, 30 or 33?

10. On which part of his body did Ronald Reagan have an operation in 1987?

Quiz 45

1. Which group released A Momentary Lapse of Reason in September 1987?

2. Which child star of the Home Alone films was born in August 1980?

3. A brand new kind of virus was first detected on 19 January 1986. Called Brain, what did it infect?

4. Actor Jake Gyllenhaal was born in December 1980. How old was he when he starred in cinemas as Donny Darko?

5. Where did Charles and Diana cruise on the Royal Yacht Britannia for their honeymoon: the Mediterranean, the Norwegian Fjords or the Caribbean?

6. Which year is MCMLXXXIX in Roman numerals?

7. When was the first London Marathon staged?

8. When was the first leap year of the 1980s?

9. Which British computer company debuted the ZX81 computer on 5 March 1981 and went on to sell 1.5 million units worldwide?

10. In which year of the 1980s was English footballer Steven Gerrard born?

Quiz 46

1. Which island nation got its own flag, for the first time, on 21 June 1985? It then discovered that the design was identical to that of the flag of the Danish rowing club.

2. Who was announced would be the new James Bond in March 1986, but ended up having to wait until another actor had played that character in two films before taking it himself?

3. The first episode of which three-film series opened in cinemas in July 1985?

4. Which well-known family was "created" in 1986?

5. Who did Argentina beat to win the 1986 FIFA World Cup? France, West Germany or Belgium?

6. Who survived being shot in St Peter's Square, Vatican City, on 13 May 1981?

7. Which actress, who died in 1986, starred in It's A Wonderful Life, and later went on to stand in for Barbara Bel Geddes as Miss Ellie Ewing, in the soap Dallas's 1984 - 85 season?

8. What was unusual about Peter Sellers' performance, as Inspector Clouseau, in 1982's Trail of the Pink Panther?

9. Which of Roald Dahl's books won the 1983 Whitbread Award for high literary merit and enjoyable reading: The Witches, The Twits or The BFG?

10. Who won Best New Artist, Song of the Year, Album of the Year and Record of the Year at the Grammy Awards of 1981? Hint: his first and last names start with the same letter.

Quiz 47

1. With which Middle-Eastern country did Israel first establish diplomatic relations on 26 January 1980?
2. Which Canadian superstar won the 1988 Eurovision Song Contest in which she was representing Switzerland?
3. Which character did Joan Collins play in the TV series Dynasty?
4. When did Mikhail Gorbachev become leader of the Soviet Union: 1983, 1985, 1987 or 1989?
5. Which QETS was a national figurehead throughout the 1980s?
6. Name the 1986-born South African athlete who competed in both the Olympic Games and Paralympic Games, and was later convicted of shooting to death his girlfriend.
7. Which long-running American life-saving series debuted with an episode called Panic at Malibu Pier?
8. Which 1987 movie about the US financial district starred Michael Douglas and Charlie Sheen, and was marketed with the slogan "Every dream has a price"?
9. Which PJPTS was a religious leader throughout the 1980s?
10. Who won 1983's Golden Globe for Best Actor in a Musical or Comedy for his role in Educating Rita?

Quiz 48

1. What was 1980 in the Buddhist calendar: 1524, 2524 or 3524?
2. Whose Island Life album debuted in December 1985?

3. Who arrived in Los Angeles at the start of his first visit to the city on 15 September 1987?

4. Why was John Hinckley Jr, who shot president Ronald Reagan in 1981, found not guilty?

5. What was Airwolf in the TV series of the same name?

6. For whom did Elizabeth and David Emanuel famously make a wedding dress in July 1981?

7. Which 1913-born British actor, who appeared in Superman, Gandhi, Battle of Britain and Von Ryan's Express, died in January 1988 at the age of 74?

8. Who played Maddie Hayes in the TV comedy series, Moonlighting?

9. Which future king and member of the British Royal Family was born on 21 June 1982?

10. Where were John Lennon's ashes scattered following his funeral in 1980?

Quiz 49

1. Which character was shot in the US TV soap Dallas on 21 November 1980?

2. Whose screenplay for Hannah and Her Sisters was a 1987 Oscar winner?

3. Which English actor, born in 1983, starred in The Adjustment Bureau, Edge of Tomorrow and Salmon Fishing in the Yemen, and took the lead role in the cinema adaptation of The Girl on the Train?

4. Who published The Handmaid's Tale in 1985?

5. In November 1985, the first ever Space Shuttle, Enterprise, was donated to the Smithsonian Institution for museum display. How many times had it been into space?

6. On 18 August 1984, Joe Kittinger became the first person to complete a solo crossing of the Atlantic by which means of transport?

7. Jaws: The Revenge was released in 1987. Had there been one two, or three previous films in the series?

8. Paul McCartney exclusively released an album in the Soviet Union in 1989. What was it called?

9. Actor Ryan Gosling was born in 1980, but in which country?

10. How many people globally are estimated to have watched the marriage of Charles and Diana on 29 July 1981?

Quiz 50

1. How many times had the Space Shuttle Challenger orbited earth before it was destroyed during launch in 1986: 95, 995, 1995 or 2995?

2. Why did 14 year old Nigel Short come to prominence on 11 January 1980?

3. Which former politician, who was Prime Minister of the United Kingdom from 1957 until 1963, and known as the Earl of Stockton, died in December 1986?

4. Nintendo released what would eventually become the Nintendo Entertainment System (NES) on 15 July 1983. What was this "family computer" called at launch?

5. By what stage name is 1986-born US singer Stefani Joanne Angelina Germanotta better known?

6. Name the British racing car driver who was born on 7 January 1985.

7. Which RW was a Greenpeace ship sunk by French agents in Auckland Harbour in 1985?

8. When did the first Boeing 757 take to the skies?

9. Which TV sci-fi series, set in the 25th century, came to the end of its two-season run in April 1981?

10. Which US president's own 58-story skyscraper opened on New York's Fifth Avenue on 30 November 1983?

Quiz 51

1. Who played Indiana Jones' father in the 1989 film Indiana Jones and the Last Crusade?
2. Which puppet-based TV show, created by Jim Henson, debuted as a co-production between British, Canadian and American broadcasters on 10 January 1983?
3. Which Liverpudlian released an October 1984 album called Give My Regards to Broad Street?
4. How did Mehmet Ali Agca come to prominence in May 1981?
5. What was He-Man's cowardly pet tiger called at the times when it had not been transformed into Battle Cat?
6. What was the name of the North Sea oil production platform destroyed by fires and explosions on 6 July 1988, killing 167 people? Pipe Alpha, Piper Beta or Piper Charlie?
7. Who played Margaret "Hot Lips" Houlihan in the TV sitcom M*A*S*H until it went off air in 1983?
8. Which country gained official independence from the United Kingdom in 1982?
9. How many days did it take to film ET: 61, 81 or 101?
10. How old was Henry Fonda when he died in Los Angeles on 12 August 1982: 66, 77, 88 or 99?

Quiz 52

1. Into whose bedroom did Michael Fagan gain unauthorised access on 9 July 1982?
2. Which Star Trek series debuted in September 1987: Star Trek The Next Generation, Star Trek Voyager or Star Trek Deep Space Nine?
3. In which harbour did the Herald of Free Enterprise capsize, resulting in the deaths of 193 people?

4. Who played lead character Jack Torrance in Stanley Kubrick's 1980 movie, The Shining?

5. Who played Will Riker in the TV series Star Trek: The Next Generation?

6. Was Pan Am Flight 103 brought down over Lockerbie by a bomb planted in a suitcase, a radio or a computer?

7. How did John Hinckley Jr come to fame in March 1981?

8. Which film, starring Matthew Broderick as a delinquent schoolboy, was released on home video in 1987?

9. What was the name of the organisation that employs Michael Knight to be its KITT-driving field agent in Knight Rider?

10. Which long-standing structure was breached on 9 November 1989?

Quiz 53

1. Which Harry Potter actor was born in July 1989: Daniel Radcliffe, Rupert Grint or Emma Watson?

2. Thomas Harris's 1988 book, The Silence of the Lambs, featured which cannibalistic serial killer?

3. To whom did Walter Mondale lose the 1984 US presidential election?

4. Which Motown Records star moved to RCA Records on 14 May for $20m, the most valuable recording deal in history at the time?

5. Who played Emmett "Doc" Brown in Back to the Future?

6. Best known for his books The Spire and Lord of the Flies, who won the Nobel Prize for Literature in 1983?

7. True or false: Glenn Close, Hugh Grant, Angelina Jolie and Colin Firth all made their cinema debuts in 1982.

8. Soprano opera singer Katherine Jenkins was born on 29 June 1980, in which country?

9. Where was the fictional character Jean-Luc Picard of Star Trek: The Next Generation born in 2305?

10. How many wedding cakes did Charles and Diana have at the celebration following their 1981 marriage: 7, 17 or 27?

Quiz 54

1. Although known as the Tiananmen Square protests, in how many cities across China did the pro-democracy protests take place? 4, 40 or 400?

2. Was the train on Princess Diana's wedding dress 15 feet, 25 feet or 35 feet long?

3. What nationality is 1986-born tennis player Rafael Nadal?

4. What kind of an empire did US president Ronald Reagan famously call the Soviet Union under Yuri Andropov's rule in 1983?

5. Who won the Academy Award for Best Director in 1981: Robert Redford, Roman Polanski or Richard Rush?

6. In which British TV series did 1982-born actor Dan Stevens play Matthew Crawley?

7. Which 1986-born British actor went on to play Cedric Diggory in Harry Potter and the Goblet of Fire, and later, vampire Edward Cullen in the Twilight films?

8. Which female actor took the lead role in 1982's Grease 2?

9. Who became leader of the Soviet Union on 11 March 1985?

10. According to a well-known TV show's opening monologue, who was "a young loner on a crusade to champion the cause of the innocent, the helpless, the powerless in a world of criminals who operate above the law"?

Quiz 55

1. Which three leaders announced that the Cold War was over on 3 December 1989?
2. Who was elected president of Zimbabwe on 4 March 1980?
3. Did Amadeus win seven, eight, nine or ten categories at the 1984 Academy Awards ceremony?
4. What was the "real" name of the character known as Face in The A-Team?
5. Is the 1987 film Dirty Dancing set in 1943, 1953, 1963 or 1973?
6. Who played Martin Riggs in the 1987 cop comedy Lethal Weapon?
7. Which graphics software company was founded on 28 February 1982?
8. Who was US president at the start of the 1980s?
9. About which Spanish city did Freddy Mercury and Montserrat Caballe sing on their October 1988 single?
10. Which Scottish comedian made his cinema debut in the 1980 movie Flash Gordon?

Quiz 56

1. How many times did the first space shuttle to orbit the Earth, Columbia, actually orbit during its maiden voyage in April 1981? 17, 27, 37 times?
2. Who made her cinema debut in Star Trek II: The Wrath of Khan before going on to star in the hit 80s comedy, Cheers?
3. Of which country was Ferdinand Marcos, who died in September 1989, the president until three years earlier?
4. What was the Elk Cloner, which emerged on 30 January as the first of its kind in the world?

5. The first film in which long-running police-based comedy series appeared on home video in December 1984?

6. What did the BA stand for in The A-Team's BA Baraccus' name?

7. Who, on 7 April 1985, became the first western pop group to perform in China?

8. In which year did the Rubik's Cube make its international debut at Earl's Court, London?

9. When Rod Stewart was mugged in Los Angeles on 26 April 1982, he lost a $50,000 car to the mugger. What kind of car?

10. Which 1987 film had the tagline "Sleep all day. Party all night. Never grow old. Never die. It's fun to be a vampire"?

Quiz 57

1. Upon its release in 1983, the third entry of which maritime film series, was marketed using the tagline "the third dimension is terror"?

2. Which former First Lady of the United States, first name Bess, died on 18 October 1982?

3. Which book by Peter Wright, former Assistant Director of MI5, caused a stir upon its publication in July 1987?

4. What reason did John Hinckley Jr give for his 1981 attempted assassination of Ronald Reagan?

5. In November 1985, which city hosted the first ever face to face meeting of Ronald Reagan and Mikhail Gorbachev?

6. Which monument did Le Parisien newspaper announce would be relocated to Euro Disney on 1 April 1986?

7. True or false: George Michael didn't perform on the 1984 Band Aid single, Do They Know It's Christmas?

8. Which 1987 New York movie saw Michael J Fox play the parts of mailroom worker Brantley Foster and his executive alter-ego Carlton Whitfield?

9. In which year was Indiana Jones and the Raiders of the Lost Ark released to cinemas?

10. Britain's first driverless railway opened on 31 July 1987. Where was it?

Quiz 58

1. Which 1983-born computer professional and former CIA employee came to global attention after leaking classified information from the National Security Agency in 2013?

2. How old is Jennifer Grey's character in Dirty Dancing: 16, 17, 21 or 22?

3. Which US president sold the rights to his autobiography to Random House for $3m on 26 November 1985?

4. On 7 December 1982, Texas carried out the United States' first execution by what means?

5. Who was originally considered to take the role of Data in Star Trek: The Next Generation before he accepted a different role in the cast?

6. Which DMD was an Oscar-winning 1989 film starring Morgan Freeman and Jessica Tandy?

7. Which global phenomenon made its international debut at the British Toy and Hobby Fair in London on 29 January 1980?

8. John Hinckley Jr, Ronald Reagan's would-be assassin, fired six bullets at the president in March 1981. How many of them hit Reagan?

9. Which actor, who went on to star in Four Weddings and a Funeral, Love Actually, Notting Hill and Bridget Jones Diary, made his cinema debut in the 1982 movie, Privileged?

10. Name the American playwright, author of A Streetcar Names Desire and Cat on a Hot Tin Roof, who died aged 71 on 25 February 1983.

Quiz 59

1. How many leaders did the Soviet Union have throughout the 1980s? One, two, three or four?
2. Where did the Space Shuttle Columbia launch from for its maiden voyage in April 1981?
3. Which actor won 1983's Golden Globe for Best Actor in a Drama Series for playing the part of Blake Carrington in Dynasty?
4. Which NR lived at the White House during the 1980s?
5. Dirty Dancing won an Academy Award for Best Original Song. Which song was that?
6. ET make just shy of $800m at the box office, but what was the budget: $10.5m, $105m or $1050m?
7. By the time he gave up the role in 1985, in how many films had Roger Moore played James Bond?
8. Did Canada gain full political independence from the United Kingdom in 1982, 1983 or 1984?
9. Which competition was won by a Swedish song called Diggi-Loo Diggi-Ley on 5 May 1984?
10. Which aquatic animation was released by Disney on 17 November 1989?

Quiz 60

1. Tom Baker made his last appearance as Time Lord Doctor Who in 1981. Who took over the role?
2. The first of the GPS navigation satellites was launched in January 1989. What does GPS stand for?
3. Who sang the title track of the 1980 film, Fame?
4. Who won an Academy Award for his portrayal of Gandhi in the 1982 film of the same name?

5. John Grisham published his first book in 1989. Was it A Time to Kill, The Pelican Brief, The Rainmaker or The Runaway Jury?

6. Which actress, born in 1984, is known for her work in the films Girl with the Pearl Earring, The Horse Whisperer and Lost in Translation?

7. Umberto II, who died in 1983, was Italy's last... what?

8. Who was appointed leader of the Soviet Union on 24 May 1982?

9. Which DD performed the theme tune to a 1985 James Bond film?

10. The first Space Shuttle officially launched in April 1981. What was it called?

Quiz 61

1. Who both wrote and directed the 1989 film The Abyss, starring Ed Harris and Mary Elizabeth Mastrantonio?

2. Which Academy Award winner, who famously played Cruella de Vil in 101 Dalmatians, made her cinema debut in 1982's The World According to Garp?

3. Was the Space Shuttle Challenger on its sixth, eighth, tenth or twelfth launch when it was destroyed in 1986?

4. Which future leader of North Korea was born on 8 January 1984?

5. The final episode of which long-running TV series, set in a Korean War field hospital, was broadcast on 28 February 1983?

6. Swedish supergroup ABBA released an album called Super Trouper in 1980. How many tracks did its original incarnation include: 10, 12 or 14?

7. How old was KFC founder, Colonel Sanders, when he died in Kentucky in December 1980?

8. Which former British colony's Parliament House opened on 9 May 1988?

9. Which SPS was the site of a 1981 assassination attempt on Pope John Paul II?

10. The computer unintentionally accessed by Matthew Broderick's character in the 1983 film WarGames was called WOPR. What did WOPR stand for?

Quiz 62

1. Which landmark home computer was launched in Las Vegas on 7 January 1982?

2. What was the nationality of writer and painter Christy Brown, who could write only with the toes of one foot, and who died in 1981?

3. Who was second in command of the Enterprise on Star Trek: The Next Generation?

4. Which boxing legend fought (and lost) his final bout on 11 December 1981?

5. Space Shuttle Columbia's maiden flight, in 1981, was delayed by a technical hitch. How many days late did it eventually lift off: 2, 20 or 22?

6. The art- and sculpture-focused Musee d'Orsay opened in Paris in 1986 in a building that was previously what?

7. Which British comedian, who went on to play a spy in the Johnny English film series, made his cinema debut in 1983 James Bond film Never Say Never Again?

8. Who produced a document in 1989 describing what would become the World Wide Web?

9. What kind of car was the time machine in Back to the Future?

10. What is the nationality of singer Jessica Simpson, who was born on 10 July 1980?

Quiz 63

1. Which airliner lost one of its jumbo jets when it was blown up over Scotland on 21 December 1988?

2. Which COF was an Oscar-winning British film released in 1981?

3. How many series of Star Trek: The Next Generation, were aired following its 1987 debut?

4. Which Irene Cara song won an Academy Award in 1983 for Best Original Song?

5. In which year did NASA astronauts make their first untethered spacewalk, was the TED conference founded, Marvin Gaye was shot dead and Sarajevo hosted the winter Olympics?

6. Which soft drink company, and American icon, opened its first bottling plant in China on 15 April 1981?

7. The group ABBA released its last ever single on 3 December 1982. What was it called?

8. Of which country was Olof Palme the prime minister at the time of his 1986 assassination? Spain, Switzerland, Swaziland or Sweden?

9. Which cartoon first appeared as a series of shorts on The Tracey Ullman Show in April 1987?

10. What was The A-Team's BA Baraccus afraid of?

Quiz 64

1. Who played Kevin Flynn, a game developer who is beamed into a computer mainframe by a digitising laser in the 1982 Disney film, Tron?

2. Which TV show's theme tune was The Good Ol' Boys?

3. In which year was Indian prime minister Indira Gandhi assassinated in New Delhi?

4.   Richard Haydn, who died in April 1985, played which character in the 1965 film of The Sound of Music?

5.   Which European city gave its name to a 1980 album and 1981 single from Ultravox?

6.   Which iconic single was released on 25 November 1984?

7.   Which movie picked up Academy Awards for Best Picture, Best Director and Best Actor in 1982?

8.   Who wrote the book 1984?

9.   Which UK police series set on the island of Jersey had its TV debut on 18 October 1981?

10. Which coffee shop opened its first branches outside of Seattle in Vancouver and Chicago in 1987?

Quiz 65

1.   By what name is Jose Bandera, whose first film role was in 1982's Labyrinth of Passion, better known?

2.   How long did a siege of the Iranian Embassy in London last in the early summer of 1980?

3.   Jesse Owens, who died in 1980, was famed for winning four gold medals at the controversial 1936 Berlin Olympics. Name any one of the events in which he won a gold?

4.   About which legendary capital of Kublai Khan's empire, did Olivia Newton-John sing, with backing from the Electric Light Orchestra, on a single release in 1980?

5.   Who released an album called Hounds of Love on 16 September 1985?

6.   Which Norwegian group's debut album, Hunting High and Low, was released on 1 June 1985?

7.   How many guests attended the 1981 wedding of Prince Charles and Lady Diana Spencer? 2,500; 3,000 or 3,500?

8.   Which JC, RR and GHWB were all US presidents in the 1980s?

9. How many pearls were sewn into Princess Diana's wedding dress? 5,000; 10,000; 15,000 or 20,000?
10. Which was 1987's highest grossing film in the US: Dirty Dancing, Fatal Attraction, or Three Men and a Baby?

Quiz 66

1. The first mobile phone call was made between the president of phone company Ameritech, and the great-grandson of Alexander Graham Bell, but when?
2. He Man gained his power by holding up his sword and shouting... what?
3. Who wrote the soundtrack for 1982's Blade Runner?
4. Was Dirty Dancing released to cinemas, home video or bookshops on 6 January 1988?
5. Which famous zoologist was found murdered in Rwanda on 26 December 1985?
6. Which medical black comedy, which ran from 1982 until 1988, was set in the fictional teaching hospital St Eligius?
7. Which Boeing airliner made its maiden flight on 26 September 1981: 737, 747, 757 or 767?
8. The 1980s saw summer Olympic Games held in Moscow, Los Angeles and which other city?
9. Who assassinated John Lennon in December 1980?
10. Which ETTE-T was a 1982 Stephen Spielberg film, the highest grossing film of all time on its release, in which Elliot makes an other-worldly friend?

Quiz 67

1. What was named Time magazine's 1983 "Man of the Year"?
2. True or false: the DeLorean Motor Company had gone out of business before its DMC-12 car was used as the basis of a time machine in the film Back to the Future?

3. Who won the Academy Award for Best Actor for his role in The Color of Money?

4. Each of these 1989 films was in the running for the Academy Award for Best Picture. Which won? Driving Miss Daisy, Born on the Fourth of July, My Left Foot, or Dead Poets Society?

5. What was first used in a criminal case in 1985?

6. On 1 July 1984, which country became the last in Europe to grant women the vote?

7. We know one reactor went into meltdown, but how many reactors were there in total at the Chernobyl nuclear power plant? One, four, eight or twelve?

8. What was the first video to play on MTV when it launched in August 1981?

9. Which car designer, founder of the company that would take his name, died in Italy in August 1988, aged 90?

10. True or false: although released in 1987, Dirty Dancing didn't feature in that year's top 10 highest grossing films in the US?

Quiz 68

1. Which movie won the Best Picture award at 1984's Academy Awards ceremony: Amadeus, A Passage to India, or The Killing Fields?

2. How many days did it take the 37 performers who appeared on the 1984 Band Aid single, Do They Know It's Christmas, to make the recording?

3. In which year of the 1980s is the film of Bret Easton Ellis's 1991 novel American Psycho set?

4. What was the name of the Soviet space station whose construction began in February 1986?

5. Whose Let's Dance album was first released on 14 April 1983?

6. Which American singer and songwriter was shot dead by his father on 1 April 1984, the day before his own 45th birthday?

7. Were there more people living in Africa or Asia at the start of the 1980s?

8. In which year was Ronald Reagan sworn in for his second term as president, Mikhael Gorbachev appointed leader of the Soviet Union and Madonna performed her Virgin tour, which kicked off in New York?

9. Who played Doctor Sam Beckett, who leaped through time to correct historical mistakes in Quantum Leap?

10. Which Minnesota singer-songwriter released his third album, Dirty Mind, in October 1980?

Quiz 69

1. Which character did 1986-born actor Shawn Pyfrom play in the US TV series Desperate Housewives?

2. Name the Farrah Fawcett, Tanya Roberts and Cheryl Ladd TV series that finished in June 1981 after 110 episodes.

3. Which supernatural comedy starring Bill Murray, Sigourney Weaver, Dan Ackroyd and Rick Moranis, opened in cinemas on 7 June 1984?

4. Which former member of Swedish supergroup ABBA released an album called Wrap Your Arms Around Me at the end of May 1983?

5. After which east-coast state was Bon Jovi's 1988 album named?

6. Whose book, The Cider House Rules, was published in 1985?

7. Which member of the Monty Python troupe died in 1989: Terry Jones, Terry Gilliam, Eric Idle or Graham Chapman?

8. Which deputy Fuhrer of the Nazi regime, who flew solo to Scotland in 1941 to try and negotiate peace with the

United Kingdom, committed suicide aged 93 in Germany's Spandau prison, where he was the only remaining inmate?

9. Whose 1988 book, The Satanic Verses, was claimed to be blasphemous, leading to the author being placed under police protection?

10. Where was the fighter pilot training school in the 1986 film Top Gun?

Quiz 70

1. To which party did Ronald Reagan belong?

2. The longest running Broadway play ever opened on 26 January 1988. It was a musical by Andrew Lloyd Webber, but which one?

3. Where was Scottish tennis player Andy Murray born on 15 May 1987?

4. Which architect, famed for his work with geodesic domes, was the second World President of Mensa until his death in 1983?

5. Which fictional twins did real-life, 1986-born twins, James and Oliver Phelps depict in the Harry Potter films?

6. The 1983 sequel to which legendary Alfred Hitchcock movie saw Anthony Perkins once again play the part of Norman Bates following the character's release from a psychiatric institution?

7. Which MSH was a volcano that erupted in Washington, US, on 18 May 1980, killing 57 people?

8. What is a super trouper, aside from the name of a 1980 single and album by Swedish pop group ABBA?

9. In which year did the group Iron Maiden release its first album, which was also called Iron Maiden?

10. Which singer and actress resigned as Miss America 1984 when nude pictures of her were published in Penthouse?

Quiz 71

1. Gerald and Betty Ford, and Henry Kissinger all made cameo appearances on which long-running US TV drama on 21 December 1983?

2. The landmark video for which Michael Jackson song debuted on MTV on 2 December 1983?

3. Which American crime drama series, centred on a private Hawaii-based investigator, end its run in 1988?

4. In which of London's places of worship were Price Charles and Lady Diana married in July 1981?

5. The first of how many satellites that would go on to form the GPS system was launched on 14 February 1989: 4, 14, 24 or 34?

6. Who played Captain HM "Howling Mad" Murdock in The A-Team?

7. For how many years was Mark Champan sent to prison for assassinating John Lennon? 5 years, 10 years or 20 years?

8. Which pop performer purchased the publishing rights for the majority of The Beatles music for $47m on 6 September 1985?

9. By what name is 1983-born athlete Mohamed Muktar Jama Farah better known?

10. Against whom did Ronald Reagan contest the US presidential election of 1980?

Quiz 72

1. Entrepreneur Ray Kroc died on 14 January 1984, aged 81. Of which restaurant chain was he the owner?

2. In which harbour did French agents bomb and sink the Greenpeace ship Rainbow Warrior on 10 July 1985?

3. On which fictional planet did the action take place in He-Man and the Masters of the Universe?

4. Which MG became a world leader in 1985?

5. Who wrote the 1980 book, Smiley's People?

6. Which subject did Robin Williams' character teach in 1989's Dead Poets Society?

7. Which actor, best known for her role as a futuristic princess, did singer Paul Simon marry on 16 August 1983?

8. Pope John Paul II was the first reigning pope to visit which country when he arrived there on 28 May 1982? Germany, Greece, Great Britain or Georgia?

9. Name the 1983 film starring Matthew Broderick as a computer genius who almost starts World War III.

10. Which future star of Sex and the City acted the title role of the film Mannequin?

Quiz 73

1. Which British-based airline made its inaugural flight on 22 June 1984?

2. On which part of Beijing were protests that lasted six weeks and six days focused between April and June 1989?

3. Which US president's son, Eric, was born on 6 January 1984?

4. Did Easter Sunday 1980 fall on 30 March, 6 April or 4 May?

5. Which director of Psycho, The Birds and Rear Window died in California on 29 April 1980?

6. When did the Sony Walkman first go on sale in the United States: 1980, 1982 or 1984?

7. Who took the male lead opposite Dolly Parton in the 1982 film, The Best Little Whorehouse in Texas?

8. The first McDonalds restaurant in a country run by a communist party opened its doors on 24 March 1988. Was it in Russia, Yugoslavia, China or Czechoslovakia?

9. Love is Strange by Mickey & Sylvia was the B-side of which massive hit from 1987?

10. Which group released the album Sweet Dreams (Are Made of This) on 4 January 1983?

Quiz 74

1. Racing drivers Lewis Hamilton and Nico Rosberg were both born in 1985. Who is older?

2. Which John Updike novel of 1984 was turned into a movie three years later starring Jack Nicholson, Cher, Susan Sarandon and Michelle Pfeiffer?

3. The slogan on posters for which 1987 movie was "Part Man, Part Machine, All Cop"?

4. Who represented the United States of America by attending the 1981 wedding of Prince Charles and Lady Diana?

5. Who was prime minister of Great Britain at the start of the 1980s?

6. Name the South African model, who was born in 1983 and shot dead in her Pretoria bathroom aged 29 by athlete Oscar Pistorius.

7. The first novel in Jilly Cooper's Rutshire Chronicles series was published in the mid-1980s. Was it called Riders, Rivals, Players or Polo?

8. Whose book, A Perfect Spy, was published in 1986?

9. In which US state was singer Justin Timberlake born in January 1981?

10. Who was awarded a knighthood in 1986 for his work in organising the Live Aid concerts?

Quiz 75

1. Over which Scottish town was Pan Am Flight 103 blown up on 21 December 1988?

2. Which southern-European country joined the European Community, later to become the EU, on 1 January 1981?

3. Two Bond films were released in 1983: Octopussy and Never Say Never Again. In which one was Bond played by Roger Moore and in which was he played by Sean Connery?

4. How many doors were there in General Lee, the car from Dukes of Hazard?

5. For playing which character in Dad's Army, will John Le Mesurier, who died in 1983, be remembered?

6. Did more people live in Africa or Europe at the start of the 1980s?

7. What was the role of Beverley Crusher on the Enterprise in Star Trek: The Next Generation?

8. Who began work on Enquire, a system that would eventually become the world wide web in its public incarnation over 10 years later, on 23 June 1980?

9. Whose book, the Alchemist, was published in 1988 and became the most translated book by a living author?

10. In which country was JG Ballard's 1984 novel Empire of the Sun set?

Quiz 76

1. Who was president of the United States for eight hours on 13 July 1985?

2. The world's longest railway tunnel, the St Gothard, opened on 5 September 1980. It's over 10 miles (16km) long, and situated in which country?

3. Alongside which entrepreneur did Per Lindstrand complete the first transatlantic crossing by hot air balloon in July 1987?

4. Which animal-based musical began an 18-year run on Broadway on 7 September 1982?

5. Name the Australian rock band, which debuted with a self-titled album in October 1980, and whose name consists of just four capital letters.

6. What was the name of the world's first 24-hour video music channel, which launched on 1 August 1981?

7. Which Australian kicked off her recording career with the release of The Loco-Motion on 4 July 1987?

8. What nationality was Jorge Luis Borges, the writer, poet and philosopher who died in Geneva in June 1986?

9. What was the job of Hawkeye Pierce, the lead character in M*A*S*H, the TV sitcom that ran until 1983?

10. Name the TV series that starred Bea Arthur, Betty White, Rue McClanahan and Estelle Getty as four retirees sharing a home.

Quiz 77

1. Which high ranking member of British intelligence, who defected to the Soviet Union in 1963, died in Moscow in May 1988?

2. Which one of the following did ABBA not release in 1980? The Winner Takes It All, On and On an On, Super Trouper or Lay All Your Love On Me?

3. Which pope's Polish birthplace was opened as a museum on 18 May 1984?

4. Who played villainous sidekick May Day in the 1985 Bond film A View to a Kill?

5. Who performed Ghostbusters, the hit song featured in the 1984 film of the same name?

6. George Michael released his first solo album in 1987. What was it called?

7. Robert Zemeckis and Bob Gale were nominated for Best Original Screenplay at the 1986 Academy Awards ceremony, for which film?

8. France and Britain signed the Treaty of Canterbury in February 1986, which defined a new frontier between the two countries. Where was the frontier located?

9. In which country is the Chernobyl power station, which went into meltdown in April 1986?

10. When was Windows 1.0 released?

Quiz 78

1. Who replaced Roger Moore in the role of James Bond?

2. Why was the city of Pripyat abandoned in April 1986?

3. From whom did Madonna file for divorce on 25 January 1989?

4. To which city's underground did The A Team supposedly escape after being "sent to prison by a military court for a crime they didn't commit"?

5. For which country was British art historian Anthony Frederick Blunt, who died in 1983, found to have been spying?

6. The Iran-Iraq war began in September 1980 and continued until when: 1984, 1986 or 1988?

7. Which novelist, author of The Name of the Rose, published Foucault's Pendulum in 1988?

8. Which British comedian suffered a massive heart attack while on live TV and died on stage on 15 April 1984?

9. What is the nationality of 1987-born footballer Lionel Messi?

10. Which country broadcast the Eurovision Song Contest for the first time on 24 April 1983?

Quiz 79

1. Was Jamie Dornan, who was born in May 1982 and went on to play Christian Grey in the film adaptation of Fifty Shades of Grey, born in Northern Ireland or the Republic of Ireland?

2. Who won the 1988 Academy Award for Best Actress for her role as Loretta Castorini in Moonstruck?

3. Which satellite television service launched across Europe on 2 February 1989?

4. On 7 August 1985, Takao Doi, Mamoru Mohri and Chiaki Mukai were chosen to be Japan's first... what?

5. What colour was the A-Team's van?

6. Austronauts Bruce McCandless and Robert Stuart became the first to do what, on 7 February 1984?

7. What was the highest grossing film of 1983 at the US box office?

8. What was the claimed maximum speed of Sinclair's one-person, battery-powered electric vehicle, the C5?

9. Who performed the theme of the 1985 Bond film A View to a Kill?

10. Complete the film title – Star Trek IV: The Voyage... where?

Quiz 80

1. In which US state was American singer Bruno Mars born in October 1985?

2. Hungarian-born swimmer and actor, Johnny Weissmuller, died in 1984. Which jungle character did he play in movies?

3. Which English actor, famed for appearing in 26 of the 31 Carry on Films, died in Camden, London, aged 62, in April 1988?

4.   How old was Francois Mitterand when elected President of France in 1981?

5.   Who played Conan the Barbarian in the 1982 film of the same name?

6.   American pop singer Nick Carter was born on 28 January 1980. Which successful band did he eventually join?

7.   What did the media dub Ronald Reagan's Strategic Defense Initiative, which was a 1983 proposal to develop technology that could intercept enemy missiles?

8.   What was the name of Marty McFly's girlfriend in Back to the Future?

9.   What did president Ronald Reagan open up for public use on 16 September 1983?

10. Which Star Wars film hit cinemas in 1980?

Quiz 81

1.   Name the battery-assisted recumbent tricycle released by Clive Sinclair on 10 January 1985.

2.   When did Dorling Kindersley publish its first book?

3.   Which of Nasa's Space Shuttles exploded 73 seconds after take off on 28 January 1986?

4.   When did Florida's EPCOT Center open for the first time?

5.   When was the last leap year of the 1980s?

6.   Who won the 1983 Golden Globe for Best Actress in a Musical or Comedy for her performance in the title role of Educating Rita?

7.   Whose single, Hello, became Motown's first million-copy seller?

8.   Who beat the Soviet Union to win the Euro 88 football championship? France, West Germany or The Netherlands?

9.   Which member of The Beatles was assassinated outside his apartment on 8 December 1980?

10. Which iconic motor company, building cars in Belfast, was put into receivership in February 1982?

Quiz 82

1. Australian soap opera Neighbours debuted in which year?
2. Which 1985-born footballer became the youngest player ever to represent England in an international match?
3. Who wrote the 1988 children's book, Matilda?
4. Author L Ron Hubbard, who died in 1986, founded the Church of Scientology in which year? 1954, 1964 or 1974?
5. Which French electronic artist released his album Revolutions in August 1988?
6. Which future California governor played Danny DeVito's twin in the 1988 film Twins?
7. Who won the Best Actor Academy Award for his role in On Golden Pond?
8. The author of Stuart Little and Charlotte's Web died in 1985. What was he called?
9. Approximately how long is ET: The Extra-Terrestrial: an hour, an hour and a half or two hours?
10. Which CD, released on 13 May 1985, became the first to ever sell a million copies?

Quiz 83

1. What sport is at the centre of the 1989 Kevin Costner film Field of Dreams?
2. How many of the three Beverley Hills Cop films were released in the 1980s?
3. In which year was British actor Tom Hiddleston born in Westminster, London?
4. Which ROTJ was a 1983 space epic of 1983 starring Mark Hammill, Harrison Ford and Carrie Fisher?

5. 1983 was the height of the format wars, when two battling home video standards were fighting for dominance. Only one survived – VHS – but what was the name of the competing format?

6. Which former rock and roll singer was inaugurated as mayor of Palm Springs, California, in January 1988?

7. Which actor, born in Vladivostok and probably best known for his role in the film of The King and I, died in New York on 10 October 1985?

8. Which specific variety of news channel first aired on cable TV on 2 May 1982?

9. Which infectious disease did the World Health Assembly agree to eradicate globally on 8 May 1980?

10. By what name was Belgian cartoonist Georges Prosper Remi, who died in March 1983, better known?

Quiz 84

1. Whose Journeyman album was released on 7 November 1989?

2. What was the occupation of Robin Williams' character in the 1989 film Dead Poets Society?

3. By the end of its run in 1983, how many episodes of Little House on the Prairie had been broadcast in total, including specials: 108, 208, 308 or 408?

4. Who released a January 1985 album called No Jacket Required?

5. For which party was Ronald Reagan nominated to run for president on 16 July 1980?

6. How old was Whitney Houston when she released her debut album in 1985?

7. Which US president's daughter, Ivanka, was born on 30 October 1981?

8. Who released an album called The Joshua Tree on 9 March

1987?

9. Which duo played a free concert in Central Park, attended by 500,000 people on 19 September 1981?

10. In which year was spreadsheet Lotus 1-2-3 launched, the internet officially founded, Tokyo Disneyland opened and Motown celebrated its 25th anniversary?

Quiz 85

1. How deep was the wreck of the Titanic when it was located in September 1985? 2000 feet; 12,000 feet or 22,000 feet?

2. In which year did Chuck Hull invent the 3D printer?

3. What day of the week was the last day of the 1980s?

4. Which British race car driver was born on 19 January 1980?

5. In which city was The Golden Girls set?

6. When was ET: The Extra-Terrestrial first released to cinemas: 1980, 1982, 1984 or 1986?

7. Which two of these sequels was released in 1986: The Karate Kid Part II, Poltergeist II, Texas Chainsaw Massacre 2, Star Trek II?

8. Which country tore down its Moscow embassy when Russian listening devices were found there: the United Kingdom, France, West Germany or the United States?

9. Which singer went home with the Golden Globe for Best Director in 1983 for her direction of Yentl?

10. Which Swedish model played the title role in the 1983 James Bond film, Octopussy?

Quiz 86

1. In which former country was tennis player Novak Djokovic born on 22 May 1987?

2. Which soft drinks company acquired Columbia Pictures in 1982?

3. Who directed 1987's Full Metal Jacket?

4. Which of The Beatles did model and actor Barbara Bach marry on 27 April 1981?

5. Which organisation was formed by Osama bin Laden on 11 August 1988?

6. When was the Internet "born"?

7. Which IJATTOD was a 1984 film starring Harrison Ford, directed by Stephen Spielberg, from a story by George Lucas?

8. Which moon of Saturn had its existence confirmed by the Voyager 1 probe on 1 March 1980?

9. Which long-running US police TV series came to the end of its run, after 12 seasons, in April 1980?

10. Which country hosted the 1982 FIFA World Cup?

Quiz 87

1. How many series of US TV show Street Hawk, which debuted in 1985, were made in total?

2. Which British poet died in May 1984, and was both buried in Cornwall and commemorated with a statue at London's St Pancras station?

3. Irish singer Brian McFadden was born on 12 April 1980. Would he later be a member of Boyzone or Westlife?

4. Which country gained legal independence from the United Kingdom on 3 March 1986, after which the UK Parliament was unable to legislate within its territory?

5. Which author, who died in 1982 and was acclaimed for writing The Man in the High Castle, as well as books used as the basis of Blade Runner, Minority Report and Total Recall? He also wrote under the pen names Richard Phillipps and Jack Dowland?

6. The first ever instance of which messy, team-based outdoor game was played at Henniker, New Hampshire, on 27 June 1981?

7. Name the science fiction author who died in 1986, leaving behind the six-volume Dune series.

8. How many countries televised the Live Aid concerts? 145, 155 or 165?

9. How many episodes, in total, were made during the first run of He-Man and the Masters of the Universe, which began in 1983 and ended in 1985? 100, 130, 200 or 230?

10. Which film about a department store window dresser who falls in love with a model was marketed using the tagline "Some guys have all the luck"?

Quiz 88

1. What was the name of Stephen Hawking's 1988 popular science book on cosmology?

2. Which US TV series, whose title character is a private detective played by James Garner, came to the end of its run on 10 January 1980?

3. The 1987 Arnold Schwarzenegger film The Running Man was based on a 1982 novel of the same name written by Stephen King under which pseudonym?

4. Whose October 1987 album was called Heaven on Earth?

5. Which singer starred opposite her real-life husband, Sean Penn, in the 1986 movie Shanghai Surprise?

6. Beverley Burns became the world's first female captain of which large passenger aircraft on 18 July 1984?

7. Which US TV show, seen by some as a competitor to Dallas, debuted on 12 January 1981?

8. Who made his film debut in 1987's Withnail and I?

9. Which company released the Amiga computer on 23 July 1985?

10. Which of the Star Wars films was released on home video in 1986?

Quiz 89

1. What day of the week was 1 January 1985?
2. By what condition was Christy Brown, the subject of the 1989 film My Left Foot, affected?
3. How many Olympic Games were held in the 1980s?
4. Who released a novel called "It" in 1986?
5. Which two countries, which share a border, joined the European Community – later to become the European Union – on 1 January 1986?
6. Is 1980-born Jake Gyllenhaal older or younger than his actor sister Maggie?
7. Which actor, who first came to the world's attention for his role in the car-based comedy Genevieve and went on to star in Reach for the Sky and Doctor in the House, died in London on 12 July 1982?
8. Why did president Ronald Reagan relinquish the presidency of the United States for eight hours on 13 July 1985?
9. What colour was General Lee, the car in the Dukes of Hazard?
10. Which country's population exceeded 1 billion for the first time in 1982?

Quiz 90

1. In which year were the Commodore 64 and Adobe Systems founded, ET debuted in cinemas, and the Falklands War began?
2. For which iconic 1980s film character did heavy smoker Pat Welsh provide the voice?

3. Which British photographer for Vogue and Vanity Fair, who also shot Queen Elizabeth II's coronation in 1953, died in January 1980?

4. What did the UK and France announce plans to build on 20 January 1986?

5. What kind of burial ground was the subject of a 1989 film based on a Stephen King book?

6. What was Sultan bin Salman Al Saud the first Arab and first Muslim to do, in June 1985?

7. From the opening dialogue of every episode of The A Team, in which year was "a crack commando unit sent to prison for a crime they didn't commit" before promptly escaping from a maximum security stockade to the Los Angeles underground?

8. Where did 19 year old pilot Mathias Rust land his Cessna in May 1987, resulting in his facing trial in September the same year?

9. How many Academy Awards did Chariots of Fire win in 1982? Two, four or eight?

10. What is the nationality of 1981-born tennis champion, Roger Federer?

Quiz 91

1. In which year was the first Band Aid single, Do They Know It's Christmas, released?

2. Which Royal Air Force flying ace who died in 1982, saw his RAF career committed to film in the movie, Reach for the Sky?

3. Who played Charlie in Charlie's Angels from the series debut in 1976 until its end in 1981?

4. In which year did the first computer virus, Brain, start to spread, the Soviet Union launch its Mir space station, and the Space Shuttle Challenger explode during launch?

5. Which 1987 movie, directed by Stanley Kubrick, has the strap line "In Vietnam the wind doesn't blow, it sucks"?

6. Rank these 1981 films in terms of box office earnings, from highest to least profitable: On Golden Pond, Superman II, Raiders of the Lost Ark.

7. Which company launched the world's first official PC on 12 August 1981?

8. Who debuted as Mitch Buchannon in 1989's Baywatch?

9. Against which country did US president Jimmy Carter announce a grain embargo in support of the EU?

10. What three modes of transport were listed in the title of the 1987 film starring Steve Martin and John Candy as a mismatched pair of travellers trying to get home for Thanksgiving?

Quiz 92

1. What was He-Man's real name?

2. Why was Ronald Reagan sworn in as president of the United States on both 20th and 21st January 1985?

3. Which famous couple did Archbishop of Canterbury, Robert Runcie, marry at St Paul's Cathedral in London on 29 July 1981?

4. In which city was the 1984 film Ghostbusters set?

5. Which Australian actress made her cinema debut in 1983's Bush Christmas and her TV debut in BMX Bandits?

6. Which actor and writer, best known for Breakfast and Tiffany's and In Cold Blood, died in August 1984?

7. Which company released the Game Boy in North America on 31 July 1989?

8. Which 1988 film won an Academy Award for Best Picture? Rain Man, Dangerous Liaisons or Working Girl?

9. Who wrote Do Androids Dream of Electric Sheep, the book on which the 1982 movie Blade Runner was based?

10. What was the name of the first book in the Jason Bourne trilogy, by Robert Ludlum, which was published in February 1980?

Quiz 93

1. Which was more populous in 1985: North America, South America, Europe or Africa?
2. Who directed and co-wrote the 1987 movie Wall Street?
3. Which poultry-based finger food did McDonalds restaurants introduce in 1983?
4. The second book in Douglas Adams' Hitchhiker's Guide to the Galaxy series was published in 1980. What was it called?
5. Which female soloist released a 1989 album called Foreign Affair?
6. In which year did France abolish capital punishment?
7. What was produced commercially for the first time on 17 August 1982?
8. What was the value of the bounty that Iran placed on Salman Rushdie's life following publication of The Satanic Verses: $1m, $2m or $3m?
9. Who did Prince Andrew, Duke of York, marry in Westminster Abbey on 23 July 1986?
10. How long did it take Lady Diana Spencer to walk up the aisle of St Paul's Cathedral for her 1981 wedding? A minute and a half, two and a half minutes or three and a half minutes?

Quiz 94

1. Which MT led the UK throughout the 1980s?
2. Name the mountaineer who died in 1986, made famous for his ascent of Everest with Edmund Hillary.

3. One of the following didn't appear on the 1984 Band Aid single, Do They Know It's Christmas. Which one? Bono (U2), Simon Le Bon (Duran Duran), Boy George (Culture Club), Paul McCartney (Beatles)

4. Where was footballer Luis Suarez born on 24 January 1987?

5. Which country's embassy in London was taken over by terrorists on 30 April 1980?

6. Which of the Indiana Jones films was released on home video in 1986?

7. What is the name of the party leader who controls the populace in George Orwell's book 1984?

8. Which character did Tom Cruise play in the 1986 film Top Gun?

9. Who, in 1983, did the Polish Communist government falsely accuse of having fathered a child?

10. Which HC was a space object that generated considerable interest when it came close to Earth in 1986?

Quiz 95

1. The first computer to use what kind of storage device went on sale in April 1986?

2. Which member of the British royal family was born on 15 September 1984?

3. When Marc Garneau launched on the Space Shuttle Challenger on 11 October 1984, he was the first person of which nationality to go into space?

4. How old was 1983-born Kim Jong-Un when he became leader of North Korea?

5. How old was John Lennon when assassinated in New York in December 1980?

6. Who did Harry meet in the title of the 1989 film starring Billy Crystal and Meg Ryan?

7. Which TESB was a 1980 film starring Harrison Ford, written by George Lucas and directed by Irvin Kershner?

8. Which member of the group Genesis released his first solo album on 9 February 1981?

9. In which month of 1980 was John Lennon assassinated?

10. In Top Gun, what was the callsign of Tom Cruise's Radar Intercept Officer?

Quiz 96

1. What kind of car was KITT in the Knight Rider TV series?

2. Which novel by Alice Walker won the 1983 Pulitzer Prize for fiction?

3. Which party did Margaret Thatcher represent throughout her prime ministership of the United Kingdom?

4. In which category was Platoon nominated, but not the winner, at the 1987 Academy Awards: Best Picture, Best Director or Best Original Screenplay?

5. Who became the first woman to be inducted into the Rock and Roll Hall of Fame: Whitney Houston, Diana Ross or Aretha Franklin?

6. Which Spanish artist, born in 1904, died on 23 January 1989?

7. When did the world's first Blockbuster video store open?

8. Which son of British Prime Minister Margaret Thatcher went missing on 11 January 1982 while competing in the Dakar Rally?

9. What was the name of the game bundled with Windows 3.1 in which the player had to uncover squares on a board without hitting hidden bombs?

10. Demonstration copies of Multi-Tool Word were distributed free on the November 1983 cover of PC World magazine. Under which name would the software later become commercially available?

Quiz 97

1. Which woman, in power throughout the 1980s, was the first female leader of a Western nation?
2. The 1987 James Bond film featured a new actor in the lead roll. The film was The Living Daylights, but who was the actor?
3. Which IJATLC was a film starring Sean Connery and Harrison Ford as father and son archaeologists?
4. Which actor known for Cable Guy, Zoolander and Meet the Parents, made his film debut in the 1987 drama Empire of the Sun?
5. Is the 1987 movie The Witches of Eastwick set in Rhode Island, New Hampshire, Connecticut or Vermont?
6. Robert Ludlum published The Bourne Supremacy in 1986. Was it the first, second or third book in the trilogy?
7. Whose 1984 biography was called Boy?
8. Which star of the TV comedy I Love Lucy died aged 77 on 26 April 1989?
9. Which film won Best Original Score at 1984's Academy Awards ceremony: A Passage to India, Purple Rain or Indiana Jones and the Temple of Doom?
10. What was Roger Moore's last Bond film? It was released in 1985.

Quiz 98

1. Which James Bond movie was released to home video on 17 March 1988?
2. Upon her marriage to Prince William, did 1982-born Catherine Middleton become the Duchess of Cambridge, Oxford or London?
3. The 1989 film See No Evil, Hear No Evil starred Richard

Pryor and Gene Wilder. One played a blind man and one a deaf man, but which was which?

4. How many Prime Ministers did the United Kingdom have during the 1980s?

5. In which 1988 film did the Phil Collins song Two Hearts feature?

6. In how many main parts was the wreck of the Titanic discovered to be when it was found in September 1985?

7. Which singer used her initials, CK, as the name of her November 1988 album release?

8. Who directed the 1985 film, Rocky IV?

9. Which 1987 film starring Patrick Swayze and Jennifer Grey was set on a holiday resort in the 1960s?

10. Which country hosted the 1988 Summer Olympics? North Korea, South Korea, China or Japan?

Quiz 99

1. Who is James Bond's main adversary in the 1985 film A View to a Kill?

2. The first film to sell more than a million copies on home video had debuted in cinemas in 1987. What was it?

3. Which member of the Bee Gees died in 1988: Andy, Barry, Maurice or Robin?

4. Which 1979 Pink Floyd album was made into an animated film, released in 1982, with illustrations from Gerald Scarfe?

5. Where were the winter Olympic Games held in 1980?

6. What nationality is 1987-born, four-time Formula One World Champion, Sebastian Vettel: German, Austrian or Swedish?

7. How many crew were lost onboard Challenger when it exploded on lift off in January 1986? Five, six or seven?

8.   Which wreck was located by an American-French expedition of 1985 led by Robert Ballard and Jean-Louis Michel?

9.   Which series won a Golden Globe for Best Drama in 1983: Dynasty, Dallas, Cagney & Lacey or Hill Street Blues?

10. Whose self-titled debut album, released in July 1983, opened with the track Lucky Star and closed with Everybody?

Quiz 100

1.   Whose scalp was burned during the filming of a January 1984 commercial for Pepsi?

2.   In which year was ciabatta bread invented in Verona by baker Francesco Favaron?

3.   Which London-based airline collapsed on 5 February 1982 with debts of $270 million?

4.   Name the spreadsheet application, once a staple of offices worldwide, which was released by Lotus on 26 January 1983.

5.   What was unique about the fuel tanks used on the first two Space Shuttle flights in April and November 1981?

6.   Who played Maria von Trapp, who died in March 1987, in the 1965 film The Sound of Music?

7.   Which character did Daniel Day-Lewis play in the 1989 film My Left Foot?

8.   Footloose, Flashdance or Dirty Dancing: which of these films was released on home video in September 1984?

9.   The first branch of which fast food chain opened in China on 12 November 1987: McDonalds, Kentucky Fried Chicken, Dominoes or Burger King?

10. Which BTTF featured Marty McFly and Doc Emmett Brown?

Check out these other great quiz books from Ovingo

www.ovingo.com

Answers

Answers to Quiz 1

1. Knight Industries Two Thousand
2. ...in the corner
3. Sarajevo
4. Betamax
5. 9
6. Windows 2
7. Liberace
8. 5bn
9. London and Philadelphia
10. CNN

Answers to Quiz 2

1. Einstein
2. The Channel Tunnel
3. West Germany
4. Dire Straits
5. George Clooney
6. Rupert Grint
7. 1985 (14 February)
8. Metro
9. perestroika
10. The Name of the Rose

Answers to Quiz 3

1. Laurence Olivier
2. $1,565
3. Like a Prayer
4. Roxette
5. Elton John
6. Deng Xiaoping
7. Gertie
8. France
9. eleventh
10. Greece

Answers to Quiz 4

1. Mr T
2. nine times
3. Tiananmen Square
4. Chris Hemsworth
5. West Germany

6. the Macintosh
7. St Bernard
8. 180
9. Westminster Abbey
10. 4.5bn (4,434,682.000)

Answers to Quiz 5

1. 1982 (bonus: 30 November)
2. Sylvester McCoy
3. scarecrow
4. Argentina
5. M
6. 2004 and 2005
7. 1983
8. Hill Street Blues
9. Ford Motor Company
10. John Smith

Answers to Quiz 6

1. Tuesday
2. Los Angeles
3. Phil Silvers
4. John Williams
5. True
6. L Ron Hubbard
7. a car (bonus: a 1958 Plymouth Fury)
8. 1982
9. Albert Speer
10. Microsoft

Answers to Quiz 7

1. Terry Waite
2. Knight Rider
3. Brad Pitt
4. Everbody
5. Hairspray
6. Anwar Sadat
7. No
8. Madonna
9. Katy Perry
10. Tokyo

Answers to Quiz 8

1. Cary Grant
2. Teen Wolf
3. Top Gun
4. 1987
5. The Living Daylights
6. Elton John
7. Andy Warhol
8. Jean Michel Jarre
9. The Dukes of Hazard
10. Stephen King

Answers to Quiz 9

1. Nevada
2. Oprah Winfrey
3. Mount St Helens
4. 8
5. 1988
6. The Terminator
7. Eva Green
8. Chariots of Fire
9. Rick Astley
10. Hungarian

Answers to Quiz 10

1. Back to the Future
2. 1988
3. Rita Hayworth
4. Carly Simon
5. Donkey Kong
6. Curt Jurgens
7. The Woman in Black
8. Research In Motion
9. Margaret Thatcher
10. Jennifer Grey

Answers to Quiz 11

1. second
2. Jersey
3. Shirley Valentine
4. Robert F Kennedy
5. Francois Mitterand
6. True
7. Robbie Keane
8. V
9. AIDS

10. London (Kings Cross)

Answers to Quiz 12

1. 4
2. Henry Moore
3. 1987
4. Paris (Marne la Vallee)
5. 1984
6. beer
7. London
8. Martin Luther King Jr
9. Daphne du Maurier
10. Turkish

Answers to Quiz 13

1. John Le Carre
2. Mirror
3. NATO
4. George Michael (for Careless Whisper)
5. Kenneth Brannagh
6. go into space
7. Allen Carr
8. Paris Hilton
9. Tom Cruise (in Endless Love)
10. Driving Miss Daisy

Answers to Quiz 14

1. John Hinckley Jr
2. Moonlighting
3. Polish
4. General Lee
5. China
6. Ozzy Osbourne
7. Yuppie
8. MacGyver
9. Q
10. Berlin

Answers to Quiz 15

1. The Fog
2. Sally Ride
3. November
4. Pac-Man
5. Mr T
6. Top Gun

7. Moscow
8. For Your Eyes Only
9. John Paul II
10. HIV/AIDS

Answers to Quiz 16

1. The Colour of Magic
2. a glass pyramid
3. Karen Carpenter
4. four
5. Romania (Nicolae Ceausescu)
6. 1985 (1 January)
7. Iran-Iraq War
8. 14
9. Fatal Attraction
10. 2

Answers to Quiz 17

1. $25,000
2. Super Mario Bros
3. New York
4. the Carringtons in Dynasty
5. Joss Stone
6. 30 years
7. 7500
8. Excellent (Bill and Ted's Excellent Adventure)
9. Jane Wyman (for Falcon Crest)
10. Willy Russell

Answers to Quiz 18

1. ballpoint pen
2. The Elephant Man
3. The Goonies
4. Charlie Hunnam
5. Sweden and Finland
6. Colin Baker
7. John Belushi
8. Liverpool
9. The Empire Strikes Back
10. Terms of Endearment

Answers to Quiz 19

1. Dustin Hoffman
2. Octopussy
3. Dalai Lama

4. Sean Connery
5. KITT
6. Linda Hamilton
7. Bon Jovi
8. Axel Foley
9. 34
10. 1981

Answers to Quiz 20

1. Barbara Cartland
2. Bob Marley
3. John Forsythe
4. North Korea
5. 36 hours (and 54 minutes)
6. 66
7. Swedish
8. Christopher Walken
9. Bishop Desmond Tutu
10. Belgium

Answers to Quiz 21

1. Margaret Thatcher
2. REM
3. seven
4. Lloyds of London
5. Steve Jobs
6. Bananas
7. Christopher Isherwood
8. Labyrinth
9. Japan
10. Fame

Answers to Quiz 22

1. Prince Charles
2. Patrick Stewart
3. Photoshop
4. MCMLXXXV
5. the grandson of Alexander Graham Bell, inventor of the telephone
6. Benny Goodman
7. Westlife
8. Mexico
9. James Cagney
10. King Jong-un (North Korea)

Answers to Quiz 23

1. Timothy Dalton
2. Lily James
3. Russian Empire
4. Dolly Parton
5. Madonna
6. in ten years
7. Wallace and Gromit
8. Kennedy Space Center, Florida
9. Indira Gandhi
10. Leonard Nimoy

Answers to Quiz 24

1. 90
2. London
3. 9
4. 1981
5. Half
6. Michael Dukakis
7. Adolf Hitler
8. 1987
9. 49
10. Annie

Answers to Quiz 25

1. BBC
2. Gorillas in the Mist
3. none
4. Edwards Air Force Base, California
5. Quattro
6. Crocodile Dundee
7. Stealth Bomber
8. Madonna
9. Discworld
10. Lech Walesa

Answers to Quiz 26

1. 3
2. 5
3. Superman
4. Kirsten Dunst
5. Soviet Union (now Russia)
6. George W Bush
7. 1981
8. The Golden Girls
9. Zac Efron

10. 727

Answers to Quiz 27

1. 90
2. Robert De Niro
3. U2
4. Fred Astaire
5. Grenada
6. Chernobyl
7. Elliot
8. Gemma Arterton
9. Airstrip One (formerly known as Great Britain)
10. Who Framed Roger Rabbit

Answers to Quiz 28

1. the lead character had cerebral palsy and could only operate his left foot
2. False: she debuted in 1992
3. Solitaire
4. George HW Bush
5. Joan Collins
6. Ian Rankin
7. Ziggy Stardust and the Spiders from Mars
8. the Soviet Union
9. Alistair MacLean
10. Cardiff

Answers to Quiz 29

1. Videodisc
2. 27
3. The Twits
4. public opinion
5. the Netherlands
6. 9
7. Margaret Thatcher
8. Jean-Luc Picard
9. Elijah Wood
10. Tom Clancy

Answers to Quiz 30

1. AIDS
2. Steven Spielberg
3. Moonwalking

4. the FIFA World Cup
5. Timothy Dalton
6. Brighton
7. Gary Lineker (6 goals)
8. Ford Motor Company
9. Rocky III
10. 9 November

Answers to Quiz 31

1. Downton Abbey
2. Michael Jackson
3. Apple Computer
4. 1981
5. Uranus
6. Beatrice
7. the Soviet Union (132 medals)
8. False: it was her third
9. Survivor
10. Best Original Screenplay

Answers to Quiz 32

1. the Berlin Wall
2. Lee Majors
3. Ford (Henry Ford II)
4. Babe
5. ABBA
6. Emeli Sande
7. Provence (A Year in Provence)
8. Kentucky Fried Chicken (KFC)
9. Chitty Chitty Bang Bang
10. The Far Side

Answers to Quiz 33

1. AIDS
2. British Airways
3. 1985
4. BA Baracus (they're members of the A-Team)
5. Macintosh
6. Sissy Spacek
7. The Commitments
8. 1988
9. Cristiano Ronaldo
10. Eddie Redmayne

Answers to Quiz 34

1. Tootsie
2. Discovery
3. The Thorn Birds
4. Goldie Hawn
5. Bill Clinton
6. Tintin
7. St Peter's Square, Vatican City
8. Bill Medley and Jennifer Warnes
9. 1987
10. London

Answers to Quiz 35

1. Ronald Reagan
2. the name of each album was also the name of the artists themselves
3. Spock
4. Global warming
5. Out of Africa
6. peace
7. Celia Johnson
8. 17 June
9. The Earth
10. symbolics.com

Answers to Quiz 36

1. Minolta
2. 1981 (bonus: 30 March)
3. helicopter
4. 65
5. Korea
6. 1972 and 1973
7. Yugoslavia
8. True
9. Evita
10. Bruce Springsteen (Born in the USA)

Answers to Quiz 37

1. Ridley Scott
2. George HW Bush
3. Katharine Hepburn
4. Tyne Daly and Sharon Gless (and Meg Foster in series 1 as Cagney)
5. Kane and Abel
6. Say You, Say Me

7. Raiders of the Lost Ark
8. Tom Hanks
9. Anwar Sadat
10. The Confederate Flag

Answers to Quiz 38

1. six
2. Bruce Willis
3. Boss Hogg
4. Prince Andrew and Sarah Ferguson
5. Blade Runner
6. ET: The Extra-Terrestrial
7. Like a Virgin
8. True
9. Chess
10. Mel Blanc

Answers to Quiz 39

1. 1984
2. the hole in the ozone layer
3. Jamaica
4. Judy
5. The Color Purple
6. Richard Branson
7. Simply Red
8. 12
9. 14 solitaire diamonds and a 12-carat blue sapphire
10. Lake Placid (New York) and Sarajevo

Answers to Quiz 40

1. The Empire Strikes Back
2. May Day
3. Ship's counsellor
4. 1985 (19 February)
5. 11
6. Tron
7. Thursday
8. Faith
9. Keira Knightley
10. Kim Kardashian

Answers to Quiz 41

1. Calgary
2. Jerusalem

3. Return of the Jedi
4. the Space Shuttle
5. True
6. it was the world's first successful portable computer
7. Dynasty
8. 13
9. it was the first mass-market computer with a graphical interface
10. Good Morning Vietnam

Answers to Quiz 42

1. Arthur Lowe
2. Cirque du Soleil
3. 1949 (on 8 June; it was written the previous year)
4. Star Trek II
5. 1989
6. Moonstruck
7. 325
8. Warren Beatty
9. Videotape
10. Manic Miner

Answers to Quiz 43

1. Roy Orbison
2. Italy
3. 98
4. 66
5. Roger Moore
6. The Sound of Music
7. a motorbike
8. $1.5m
9. Teri Hatcher
10. it was the name of the space shuttle that made its maiden flight on that day

Answers to Quiz 44

1. U2
2. writer
3. Doctor Who
4. Pierce Brosnan
5. Frodo Baggins
6. Pixar
7. Sierra
8. 1988

9. 33
10. prostate

Answers to Quiz 45

1. Pink Floyd
2. Macaulay Culkin
3. computer virus
4. 21
5. the Mediterranean
6. 1989
7. 1981 (bonus: on 29 March)
8. 1980
9. Sinclair Research
10. 1980 (30th May)

Answers to Quiz 46

1. Greenland
2. Pierce Brosnan
3. Back to the Future
4. The Simpsons
5. West Germany
6. Pope John Paul II
7. Donna Reed
8. he died before it was made, so his performance was entirely constructed from scenes deleted from previous films
9. The Witches
10. Christopher Cross

Answers to Quiz 47

1. Egypt
2. Celine Dion
3. Alexis Colby
4. 1985
5. Queen Elizabeth II
6. Oscar Pistorious
7. Baywatch
8. Wall Street
9. Pope John Paul the Second
10. Michael Caine

Answers to Quiz 48

1. 2524
2. Grace Jones
3. Pope John Paul II

4. by reason of insanity
5. helicopter (bonus: a Bell 222)
6. Lady Diana Spencer
7. Trevor Howard
8. Cybill Shepherd
9. Prince William
10. Central Park, New York

Answers to Quiz 49

1. JR Ewing
2. Woody Allen
3. Emily Blunt
4. Margaret Atwood
5. never
6. Hot air balloon
7. 3
8. Back in the USSR
9. Canada
10. 750m

Answers to Quiz 50

1. 995
2. he was the youngest person to be awarded an International Chess Master degree
3. Harold Macmillan
4. Famicom
5. Lady Gaga
6. Lewis Hamilton
7. Rainbow Warrior
8. 1982 (bonus: 19 February)
9. Buck Rogers in the 25th Century
10. Donald Trump

Answers to Quiz 51

1. Sean Connery
2. Fraggle Rock
3. Paul McCartney
4. he attempted to assassinate Pope John Paul II
5. Cringer
6. Piper Alpha
7. Loretta Swit
8. Canada
9. 61
10. 77

Answers to Quiz 52

1. Queen Elizabeth II
2. Star Trek: The Next Generation
3. Zeebrugge (Belgium)
4. Jack Nicholson
5. Jonathan Frakes
6. a radio
7. he shot Ronald Reagan
8. Ferris Bueller's Day Off
9. the Foundation for Law and Government (FLAG)
10. The Berlin Wall

Answers to Quiz 53

1. Daniel Radcliffe
2. Hannibal Lecter
3. Ronald Reagan
4. Diana Ross
5. Christopher Lloyd
6. William Golding
7. False. The first three did, but not Colin Firth
8. Wales (United Kingdom)
9. France (La Barre)
10. 27

Answers to Quiz 54

1. 400
2. 25 feet
3. Spanish
4. an Evil Empire
5. Robert Redford
6. Downton Abbey
7. Robert Pattinson
8. Michelle Pfeiffer
9. Mikhail Gorbachev
10. Michael Knight in Knight Rider

Answers to Quiz 55

1. George HW Bush, Mikhail Gorbachev and Margaret Thatcher
2. Robert Mugabe
3. 8
4. Templeton Peck
5. 1963
6. Mel Gibson

7. Adobe Systems
8. Jimmy Carter
9. Barcelona
10. Robbie Coltrane

Answers to Quiz 56

1. 37
2. Kirstie Alley
3. the Philippines
4. a computer virus
5. Police Academy
6. Bad Attitude
7. Wham
8. 1980
9. Porsche
10. The Lost Boys

Answers to Quiz 57

1. Jaws 3-D
2. Bess Truman
3. Spy Catcher
4. he wanted to impress the actor Jodie Foster
5. Geneva
6. The Eiffel Tower
7. False
8. The Secret of My Success
9. 1981
10. London Docklands

Answers to Quiz 58

1. Edward Snowden
2. 17
3. Ronald Reagan
4. Lethal injection
5. Patrick Stewart
6. Driving Miss Daisy
7. Rubik's Cube
8. one
9. Hugh Grant
10. Tennessee Williams

Answers to Quiz 59

1. four
2. Kennedy Space Center, Florida
3. John Forsythe

4.   Nancy Reagan
5.   (I've Had) The Time of My Life
6. $10.5m
7.   seven
8.   1982
9.   the Eurovision Song Contest
10. The Little Mermaid

Answers to Quiz 60

1.   Peter Davison
2.   Global Positioning System
3.   Irene Cara
4.   Ben Kingsley
5.   A Time to Kill
6.   Scarlett Johansson
7.   the last king of Italy
8.   Yuri Andropov
9.   Duran Duran
10. Columbia

Answers to Quiz 61

1.   James Cameron
2.   Glenn Close
3.   10th
4.   Kim Jong-un
5.   M*A*S*H
6.   10
7.   90
8.   Australia (Canberra)
9.   St Peter's Square
10. War Operation Plan Response

Answers to Quiz 62

1.   Commodore 64
2.   Irish
3.   William Riker
4.   Muhammad Ali
5.   2
6.   a railway station
7.   Rowan Atkinson
8.   Tim Berners-Lee
9.   DeLorean
10. American

Answers to Quiz 63

1.   Pan Am
2.   Chariots of Rire

3.   7
4.   Flashdance… What a Feeling
5.   1984
6.   Coca-Cola
7.   Under Attack
8.   Sweden
9.   The Simpsons
10. flying

Answers to Quiz 64

1.   Jeff Bridges
2.   The Dukes of Hazard
3.   1984
4.   Maximilian "Max" Detweiler
5.   Vienna
6.   Do They Know It's Christmas (Band Aid)
7.   Gandhi
8.   George Orwell
9.   Bergerac
10. Starbucks

Answers to Quiz 65

1.   Antonio Banderas
2.   six days (30 April to 5 May)
3.   accept 100m, 200m, 4x100m relay or long jump
4.   Xanadu
5.   Kate Bush
6.   a-ha
7.   3,500
8.   Jimmy Carter, Ronald Reagan, George HW Bush
9.   10,000
10. Three Men and a Baby

Answers to Quiz 66

1.   1983 (bonus: 13 October)
2.   By the Power of Grayskull
3.   Vangelis
4.   home video
5.   Dian Fossey
6.   St Elsewhere
7.   767
8.   Seoul
9.   John Lennon
10. ET The Extra-Terrestrial

Answers to Quiz 67

1. the computer
2. True
3. Paul Newman
4. Driving Miss Daisy
5. DNA evidence
6. Liechtenstein
7. four
8. Video Killed the Radio Star by Buggles
9. Enzo Ferrari
10. True

Answers to Quiz 68

1. Amadeus
2. 1 (from 11am until 7pm on 25 November 1984)
3. 1987
4. Mir
5. David Bowie
6. Marvin Gaye
7. Asia
8. 1985
9. Scott Bakula
10. Prince

Answers to Quiz 69

1. Andrew Van de Kamp
2. Charlie's Angels
3. Ghostbusters
4. Agnetha Faltskog
5. New Jersey
6. John Irving
7. Graham Chapman
8. Rudolf Hess
9. Salman Rushdie
10. Miramar, California (San Diego)

Answers to Quiz 70

1. Republican
2. The Phantom of the Opera
3. Glasgow
4. Buckminster Fuller
5. Fred and George Weasley
6. Psycho (the sequel was Psycho II)
7. Mount Saint Helens
8. a kind of spotlight used in stadium concerts
9. 1980
10. Vanessa Williams

Answers to Quiz 71

1. Dynasty
2. Thriller
3. Magnum PI
4. St Paul's Cathedral
5. 24
6. Dwight Schultz
7. 20 years
8. Michael Jackson
9. Mo
10. Jimmy Carter

Answers to Quiz 72

1. McDonalds
2. Auckland, New Zealand
3. Eternia
4. Mikhail Gorbachev
5. John le Carre
6. English
7. Carrie Fisher
8. Great Britain
9. WarGames
10. Kim Cattrall

Answers to Quiz 73

1. Virgin Atlantic Airways
2. Tiananmen Square
3. Donald Trump
4. 6 April
5. Alfred Hitchcock
6. 1980 (bonus: on 25 June)
7. Burt Reynolds
8. Yugoslavia
9. (I've Had) The Time of My Life
10. Eurythmics

Answers to Quiz 74

1. Lewis Hamilton
2. The Witches of Eastwick
3. RoboCop
4. Nancy Reagan

5. Margaret Thatcher
6. Reeva Steenkamp
7. Riders
8. John Le Carre
9. Tennessee
10. Bob Geldof

Answers to Quiz 75

1. Lockerbie
2. Greece
3. Roger Moore in Octopussy; Sean Connery in Never Say Never Again
4. two
5. Sergeant Wilson
6. Europe
7. Chief medical officer
8. Tim Berners-Lee
9. Paolo Coelho
10. Japan

Answers to Quiz 76

1. George HW Bush (while Ronald Reagan was undergoing an operation)
2. Switzerland
3. Richard Branson
4. Cats
5. INXS
6. MTV
7. Kylie Minogue
8. Argentinian
9. chief surgeon
10. The Golden Girls

Answers to Quiz 77

1. Kim Philby
2. Lay All Your Love On Me (it was released in 1981)
3. Pope John Paul II
4. Grace Jones
5. Ray Parker Jr
6. Faith
7. Back to the Future
8. half way along the Channel Tunnel
9. Ukraine
10. 1985 (November 20th)

Answers to Quiz 78

1. Timothy Dalton
2. it was the closest city to the nuclear power plant at Chernobyl
3. Sean Penn
4. Los Angeles
5. the Soviet Union
6. 1988
7. Umberto Eco
8. Tommy Cooper
9. Argentinian
10. Australia

Answers to Quiz 79

1. Northern Ireland
2. Chernobyl
3. Sky
4. astronauts
5. black with a red stripe
6. make an untethered space walk
7. Return of the Jedi
8. 15mph (24km/h)
9. Duran Duran
10. Home

Answers to Quiz 80

1. Hawaii
2. Tarzan
3. Kenneth Williams
4. 64
5. Arnold Schwarzenegger
6. The Backstreet Boys
7. Star Wars
8. Jennifer (Parker)
9. GPS (Global Positioning System)
10. Episode V: The Empire Strikes Back

Answers to Quiz 81

1. Sinclair C5
2. 1982
3. Challenger
4. 1982 (bonus: 1 October)
5. 1988
6. Julie Walters
7. Lionel Richie
8. The Netherlands

9. John Lennon
10. DeLorean Motor Company

Answers to Quiz 82

1. 1985 (18 March)
2. Wayne Rooney
3. Roald Dahl
4. 1954
5. Jean-Michel Jarre
6. Arnold Schwarzenegger
7. Henry Fonda
8. EB White
9. two hours (114 minutes)
10. Brothers in Arms by Dire Straits

Answers to Quiz 83

1. baseball
2. two
3. 1981
4. Return of the Jedi
5. Betamax
6. Sonny Bono
7. Yul Brynner
8. The Weather Channel
9. Smallpox
10. Herge

Answers to Quiz 84

1. Eric Clapton
2. teacher
3. 208
4. Phil Collins
5. Republican
6. 21
7. Donald Trump
8. U2
9. Simon and Garfunkel
10. 1983

Answers to Quiz 85

1. 12,000 feet
2. 1983
3. Sunday
4. Jenson Button
5. Miami
6. 1982

7. Star Trek II
8. the United States
9. Barbra Streisand
10. Maud Adams

Answers to Quiz 86

1. Yugoslavia
2. Coca-Cola
3. Stanley Kubrick
4. Ringo Starr
5. Al-Qaeda
6. 1983 (bonus: 1 January)
7. Indiana Jones and the Temple of Doom
8. Janus
9. Hawaii Five-0
10. Spain

Answers to Quiz 87

1. 1
2. John Betjeman
3. Westlife
4. Australia
5. Philip K Dick
6. paintball
7. Frank Herbert
8. 165
9. 130
10. Mannequin

Answers to Quiz 88

1. A Brief History of Time
2. The Rockford Files
3. Richard Bachman
4. Belinda Carlisle
5. Madonna
6. Boeing 747
7. Dynasty
8. Richard E Grant
9. Commodore
10. Return of the Jedi

Answers to Quiz 89

1. Tuesday
2. cerebral palsy
3. 5 (1980 summer, 1980 winter,

1984 summer, 1984 winter, 1988 summer)
4. Stephen King
5. Spain and Portugal
6. younger (she was born in 1977)
7. Kenneth More
8. he was undergoing surgery to remove cancerous polyps from his colon, and so fully sedated
9. orange (although the official name of the colour was Flame Red)
10. China

Answers to Quiz 90

1. 1982
2. ET
3. Cecil Beaton
4. the Channel Tunnel
5. Pet Sematary
6. fly into space
7. 1972
8. Red Square, Moscow
9. four
10. Swiss

Answers to Quiz 91

1. 1984
2. Douglas Bader
3. John Forsythe
4. 1986
5. Full Metal Jacket
6. Raiders of the Lost Ark, On Golden Pond, Superman II
7. IBM
8. David Hasselhoff
9. The Soviet Union
10. Planes, Trains and Automobiles

Answers to Quiz 92

1. Prince Adam
2. 20th was a Sunday, so the swearing-in was private. It was repeated publicly the next day
3. Prince Charles and Lady Diana Spencer
4. New York
5. Nicole Kidman

6. Truman Capote
7. Nintendo
8. Rain Man
9. Philip K Dick
10. The Bourne Identity

Answers to Quiz 93

1. Europe (706m people)
2. Oliver Stone
3. Chicken McNuggets
4. The Restaurant at the End of the Universe
5. Tina Turner
6. 1981
7. compact discs
8. $3m
9. Sarah Ferguson
10. three and a half minutes

Answers to Quiz 94

1. Margaret Thatcher
2. Tenzing Norgay
3. Paul McCartney
4. Uruguay (Salto)
5. Iran
6. Indiana Jones and the Temple of Doom
7. Big Brother
8. Maverick (Pete Mitchell)
9. Pope John Paul II
10. Halley's Comet

Answers to Quiz 95

1. 3.5in floppy disks
2. Prince Harry
3. Canadian
4. 32
5. 40
6. Sally (When Harry Met Sally…)
7. The Empire Strikes Back
8. Phil Collins
9. December
10. Goose

Answers to Quiz 96

1. Pontiac Firebird Trans Am

2. The Color Purple
3. Conservative Party
4. Best Original Screenplay
5. Aretha Franklin
6. Salvador Dali
7. 1985 (19 October)
8. Mark Thatcher
9. Minesweeper
10. Microsoft Word

Answers to Quiz 97

1. Margaret Thatcher
2. Timothy Dalton
3. Indiana Jones and the Last Crusade
4. Ben Stiller
5. Rhode Island
6. cooond
7. Roald Dahl
8. Lucille Ball
9. A Passage to India
10. A View To a Kill

Answers to Quiz 98

1. The Living Daylights
2. Cambridge
3. Richard Pryor's character was blind;
   Gene Wilder's was deaf
4. 1
5. Buster
6. two
7. Chaka Khan
8. Sylvester Stallone
9. Dirty Dancing
10. South Korea

Answers to Quiz 99

1. Max Zorin
2. Dirty Dancing
3. Andy
4. The Wall
5. Lake Placid, New York
6. German
7. seven
8. RMS Titanic
9. Dynasty
10. Madonna

Answers to Quiz 100

1. Michael Jackson
2. 1982
3. Laker Airways
4. 1-2-3
5. they were the only two tanks to
   have ever been painted white; on
   all other Shuttle flights, the tanks
   have been unpainted
6. Julie Andrews
7. Christy Brown
8. Footloose
9. Kentucky Fried Chicken
10. Back to the Future

Check out these other great quiz books from Ovingo
www.ovingo.com